Contents

About
Vocabulary Centers
Grades 5-6

What's Great About This Book

Centers are a wonderful, fun way for students to practice important skills. The 12 centers in this book are self-contained and portable. Students may work at a desk, at a table, or even on the floor. Once you've made the centers, they're ready to use any time.

What's in This Book

Teacher and student directions include how to make and use the center

Full-color task cards and games

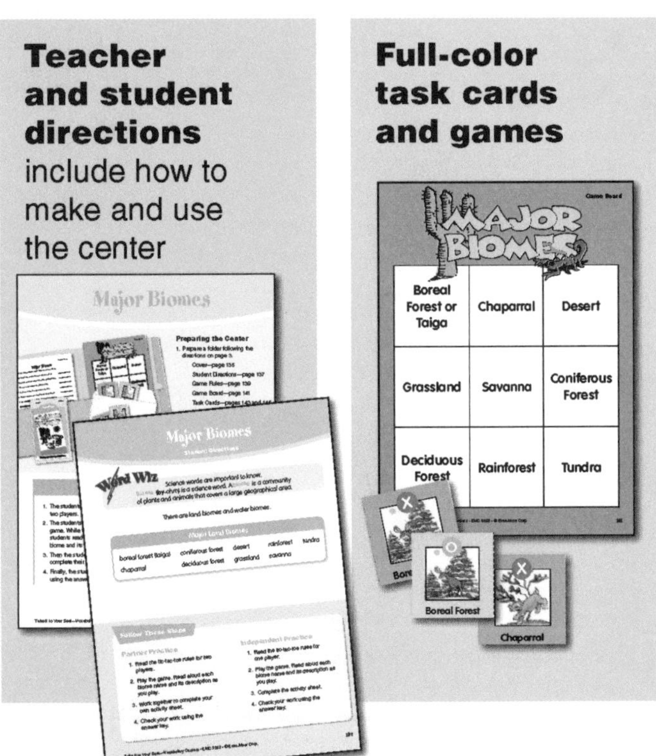

Reproducible activity sheets to practice vocabulary skills

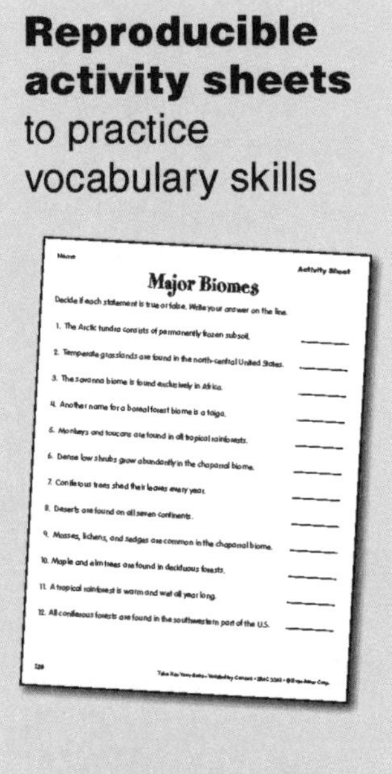

Self-checking answer keys

How to Use the Centers

The centers are intended for skill practice, not to introduce skills. It is important to model the use of each center before students do the task independently.

Questions to Consider:

- Will students select a center, or will you assign the centers?
- Will there be a specific block of time for centers, or will the centers be used throughout the day?
- Where will you place the centers for easy access by students?
- What procedure will students use when they need help with the center tasks?
- How will you track the tasks and centers completed by each student?

Making a File Folder Center

Folder centers are easily stored in a box or file crate. Students take a folder to their desks to complete the task.

Materials:

- folder with pockets
- envelopes
- marking pens and pencils
- scissors
- stapler
- glue or two-sided tape
- small objects for markers (e.g., dried beans, pennies, etc.)

Steps to Follow:

1. Laminate the cover. Tape it to the front of the folder.
2. Laminate the student directions page. Tape it to the back of the folder.
3. Laminate the self-checking answer key for each center. Cut the page in half. Staple the cover on top of the answer key. Place the answer key in the left-hand pocket.
4. Place activity sheets and any other supplies in the left-hand pocket.
5. Laminate the task cards and puzzle pieces. Place each set in a labeled envelope in the right-hand pocket.
6. If needed for a center, laminate the sorting mat or game board and place it in the right-hand pocket of the folder.

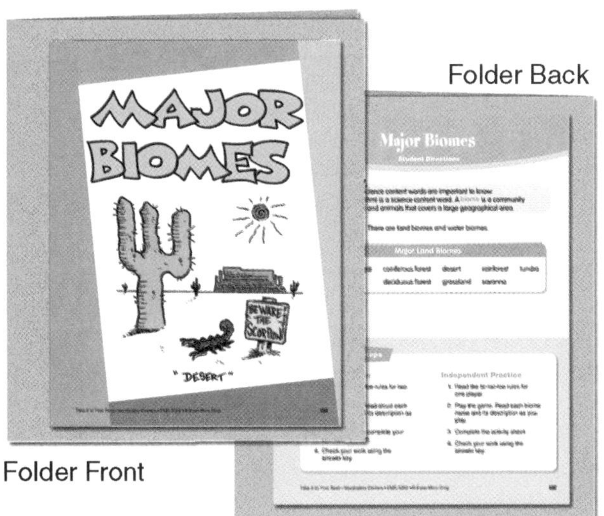

Folder Back

Folder Front

Center Checklist

Centers	Student Names											
Exciting Synonyms												
Antonym Expert												
Homophone Play												
Presenting Prefixes												
All About Acronyms												
Analyzing Analogies												
Dramatic Compounds												
A Mishmash of Words												
Major Biomes												
Geometry Terms												
French Sayings												
Choosing Homographs												

Exciting Synonyms

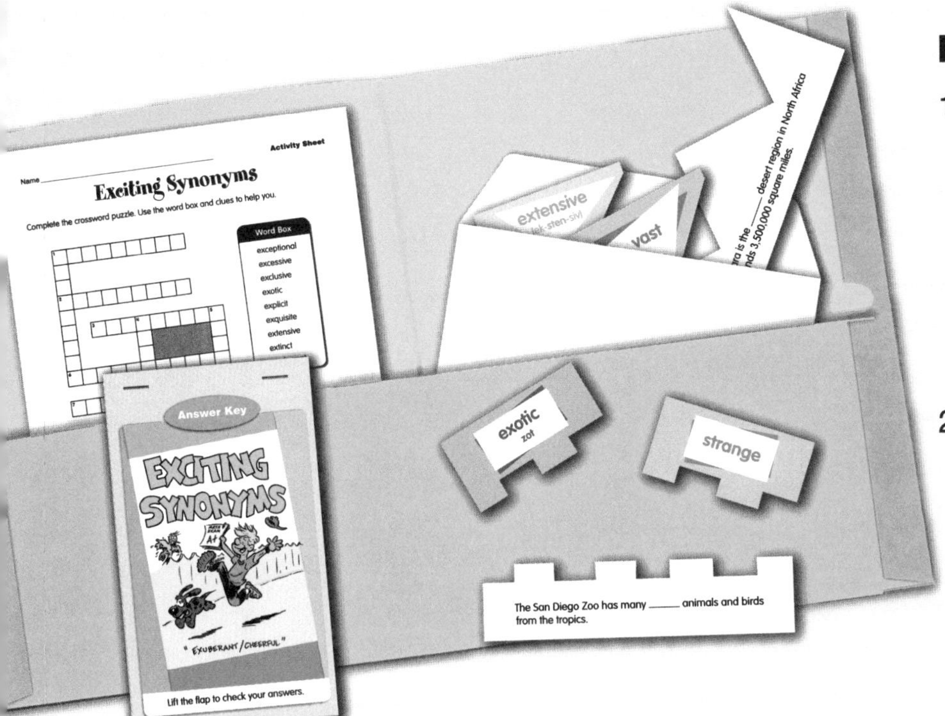

Preparing the Center

1. Prepare a folder following the directions on page 3.

    Cover—page 7

    Student Directions—page 9

    Puzzle Pieces—pages 11–15

    Answer Key—page 17

2. Reproduce a supply of the activity sheet on page 6. Place copies in the left-hand pocket of the folder.

Partner Practice

1. The students sort the puzzle pieces into three piles—words with pronunciations, words, and sentences.
2. Working together, the students match two synonyms and the corresponding sentence to make a three-part puzzle.
3. The students repeat Step 2 to complete the other eight puzzles. Encourage the students to read aloud each sentence twice, substituting each synonym that completes it.
4. Then the students work cooperatively to complete their own activity sheet.
5. Finally, the students check their work using the answer key.

Independent Practice

1. The student sorts the puzzle pieces into three piles—words with pronunciations, words, and sentences.
2. The student matches two synonyms and the corresponding sentence to make a three-part puzzle.
3. The student repeats Step 2 to complete the other eight puzzles. Encourage the student to read aloud each sentence twice, substituting each synonym that completes it.
4. Then the student completes the activity sheet.
5. Finally, the student self-checks by using the answer key.

Name ____________________ **Activity Sheet**

Exciting Synonyms

Complete the crossword puzzle. Use the word box and clues to help you.

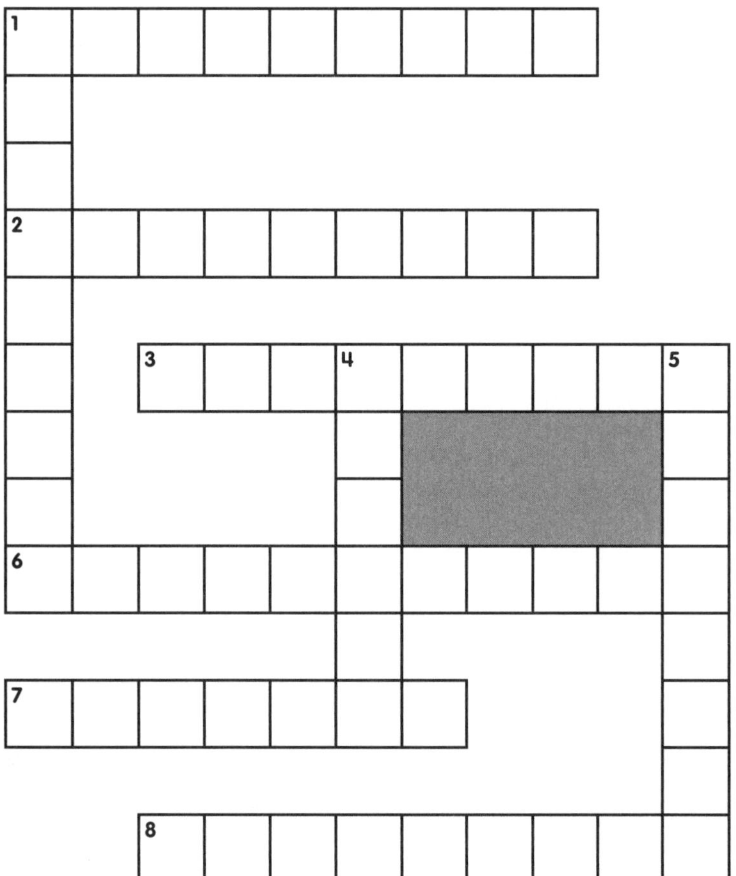

Word Box

exceptional
excessive
exclusive
exotic
explicit
exquisite
extensive
extinct
exuberant

Across

1. beautiful
2. absolute
3. overabundant
6. rare
7. nonexistent
8. cheerful

Down

1. vast
4. strange
5. clear

EXCITING SYNONYMS

" EXUBERANT / CHEERFUL "

Exciting Synonyms

Student Directions

Synonyms are words that mean the same or nearly the same.

The words **beautiful** and **exquisite** are synonyms.

They have the same meaning.

Exquisite means "very beautiful or lovely."

Your deep-blue sapphire ring is **beautiful**.

Your deep-blue sapphire ring is **exquisite**.

Follow These Steps

Partner Practice

1. Sort the puzzle pieces into three piles—words with pronunciations, words, and sentences.
2. Match two synonyms and a sentence to complete a puzzle. Take turns reading the sentence aloud twice, using each synonym that correctly completes it.
3. Repeat Step 2 to complete the other eight puzzles.
4. Work together to complete your own activity sheet.
5. Check your work using the answer key.

Independent Practice

1. Sort the puzzle pieces into three piles—words with pronunciations, words, and sentences.
2. Match two synonyms and a sentence to complete a puzzle. Read the sentence aloud twice, using each synonym that correctly completes it.
3. Repeat Step 2 to complete the other eight puzzles.
4. Complete the activity sheet.
5. Check your work using the answer key.

rare

Melanie shows ______ talent in her ability to play the piano.

overabundant

Jeremy felt sick after eating an ______ amount of pizza.

(ek-**skloo**-siv)

absolute

No other newspaper could print the story because the *Times* reporter had ______ rights to it.

Exciting Synonyms
EMC 3352 • © Evan-Moor Corp.

Exciting Synonyms
EMC 3352 • © Evan-Moor Corp.

Exciting Synonyms
EMC 3352 • © Evan-Moor Corp.

Exciting Synonyms
EMC 3352 • © Evan-Moor Corp.

Exciting Synonyms
EMC 3352 • © Evan-Moor Corp.

Exciting Synonyms
EMC 3352 • © Evan-Moor Corp.

Exciting Synonyms
EMC 3352 • © Evan-Moor Corp.

Exciting Synonyms
EMC 3352 • © Evan-Moor Corp.

Exciting Synonyms
EMC 3352 • © Evan-Moor Corp.

exotic
(eg-**zot**-ik)

strange

The San Diego Zoo has many ______ animals and birds from the tropics.

exquisite
(ek-**skwiz**-it)

beautiful

The beaded gown that the movie star wore to the Academy Awards was ______.

extensive
(ek-**sten**-siv)

vast

The Sahara is the ______ desert region in North Africa that extends 3,500,000 square miles.

Exciting Synonyms

EMC 3352 • © Evan-Moor Corp.

Exciting Synonyms

EMC 3352 • © Evan-Moor Corp.

Exciting Synonyms

EMC 3352 • © Evan-Moor Corp.

Exciting Synonyms

EMC 3352 • © Evan-Moor Corp.

Exciting Synonyms

EMC 3352 • © Evan-Moor Corp.

Exciting Synonyms

EMC 3352 • © Evan-Moor Corp.

Exciting Synonyms

EMC 3352 • © Evan-Moor Corp.

Exciting Synonyms

EMC 3352 • © Evan-Moor Corp.

Exciting Synonyms

EMC 3352 • © Evan-Moor Corp.

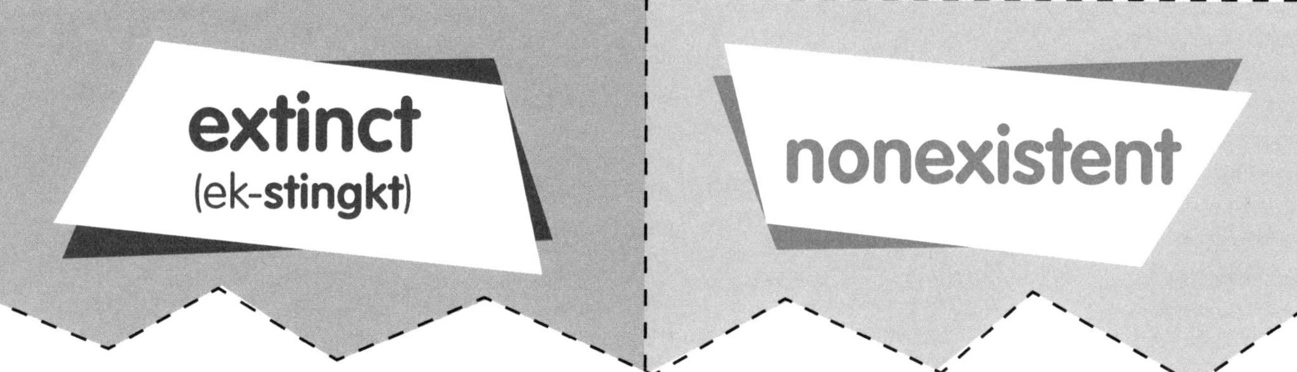

Dinosaurs once walked the Earth, but now they are ______.

exuberant
(eg-**zoo**-bur-unt)

cheerful

My sister Kathleen felt ______ when she represented Iowa at the National Spelling Bee.

explicit
(ek-**spliss**-it)

clear

I gave the taxi driver ______ directions for getting from the airport to my house.

Exciting Synonyms

EMC 3352 • © Evan-Moor Corp.

Exciting Synonyms

EMC 3352 • © Evan-Moor Corp.

Exciting Synonyms

EMC 3352 • © Evan-Moor Corp.

Exciting Synonyms

EMC 3352 • © Evan-Moor Corp.

Exciting Synonyms

EMC 3352 • © Evan-Moor Corp.

Exciting Synonyms

EMC 3352 • © Evan-Moor Corp.

Exciting Synonyms

EMC 3352 • © Evan-Moor Corp.

Exciting Synonyms

EMC 3352 • © Evan-Moor Corp.

Lift the flap to check your answers.

Exciting Synonyms

1e	x	q	u	i	s	i	t	e		
x										
t										
2e	x	c	l	u	s	i	v	e		
n										
s		3e	x	c	4e	s	s	i	v	5e
i					x					x
v					o					p
6e	x	c	e	p	t	i	o	n	a	l
					i					i
7e	x	t	i	n	c	t				c
										i
		8e	x	u	b	e	r	a	n	t

Antonym Expert

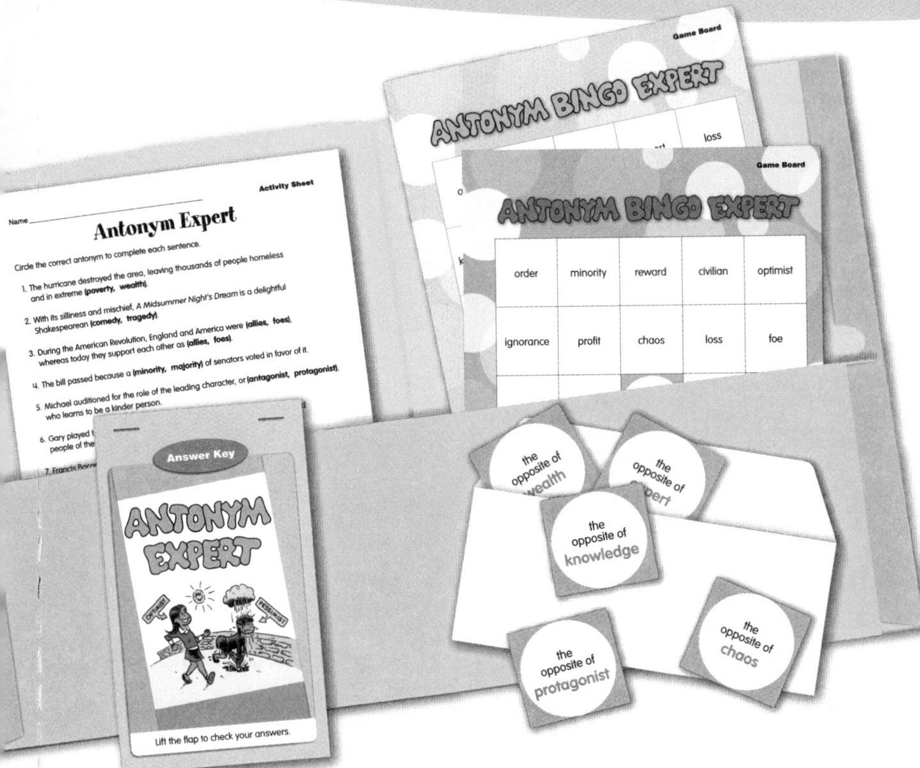

Preparing the Center

1. Prepare a folder following the directions on page 3.

   Cover—page 21

   Student Directions—page 23

   Game Rules—page 25

   Game Boards—pages 27 and 29

   Clue Cards—pages 31 and 33

   Answer Key—page 35

2. Reproduce a supply of the activity sheet on page 20. Place copies in the left-hand pocket of the folder.

Partner Practice

1. The students read the bingo rules for two players.
2. The students decide which of them will be the leader for the game. The leader also plays.
3. Each student takes a game board and some markers. (Use colored paper squares, pennies, or dried beans for markers.)
4. The students follow the rules to play Antonym Bingo Expert.
5. Then students work cooperatively to complete their own activity sheet.
6. Finally, the students check their work using the answer key.

Independent Practice

1. The student reads the bingo rules for one player.
2. The student takes a game board and some markers. (Use colored paper squares, pennies, or dried beans for markers.)
3. The student follows the rules to play Antonym Bingo Expert.
4. Then the student completes the activity sheet.
5. Finally, the student self-checks by using the answer key.

Antonym Expert

Circle the correct antonym(s) to complete each sentence.

1. The hurricane destroyed the area, leaving thousands of people homeless and in extreme **(poverty, wealth)**.

2. With its silliness and mischief, *A Midsummer Night's Dream* is a delightful Shakespearean **(comedy, tragedy)**.

3. During the American Revolution, England and America were **(allies, foes)**, whereas today they support each other as **(allies, foes)**.

4. The bill passed because a **(minority, majority)** of senators voted in favor of it.

5. Michael auditioned for the role of the leading character, or **(antagonist, protagonist)**, who is a hero.

6. Gary played the role of the greedy **(protagonist, antagonist)** who cheated people of their earnings.

7. Francis Bacon, the philosopher, encouraged learning and wrote, **("Knowledge, Ignorance)** itself is power."

8. Pilgrim teachers put sticks in boys' mouths as a **(reward, punishment)** for whispering during class.

9. George Washington was the commander-in-chief of the country's first **(military, civilian)** troops, called the American Continental Army.

10. My dad's business was doing well and showed a **(loss, profit)** after he had paid the expenses.

11. During the storm, the school alarm squealed and then the lights went out, resulting in total **(order, chaos)** in the classroom.

ANTONYM EXPERT

Antonym Expert

Student Directions

Antonyms are words that have opposite meanings.

Optimist and **pessimist** are antonyms.

Jack was an **optimist** and felt hopeful about making friends at his new school.

Jack was a **pessimist** and felt doubtful about making friends at his new school.

Follow These Steps

Partner Practice

1. Both players take a game board and some markers.
2. Read the bingo rules for two players.
3. Play Antonym Bingo Expert.
4. Work together to complete your own activity sheet.
5. Check your work using the answer key.

Independent Practice

1. Take a game board, some markers, and the clue cards.
2. Read the bingo rules for one player.
3. Play Antonym Bingo Expert.
4. Complete the activity sheet.
5. Check your work using the answer key.

Antonym Bingo Expert

Rules for 2 Players:

1. Choose a leader. The leader reads the clue cards and plays the game.
2. Shuffle the clue cards and stack them clue side up.
3. Take a bingo card and some markers. Place a marker on the FREE space.
4. The leader reads the top card aloud and sets it aside for checking later.
5. Find the antonym, or opposite, of the clue card and cover the word with a marker.
6. Repeat the process until one player covers a row of antonyms and calls out, "Antonym Bingo Expert!" The covered row may be horizontal, vertical, or diagonal.
7. The leader checks the covered words on the game board against the answers on the backs of the clue cards.
8. If the antonyms match, the player wins and becomes the leader for the next round.

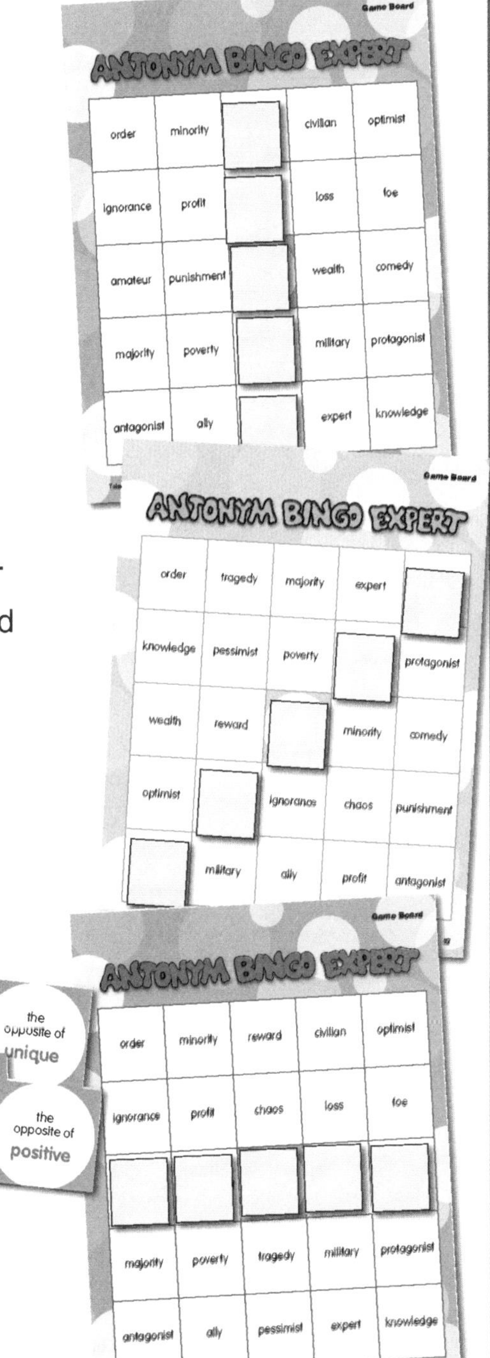

Rules for 1 Player:

1. Shuffle the clue cards and stack them clue side up.
2. Take a bingo card and some markers. Place a marker on the FREE space.
3. Read the top card aloud and set it aside for checking later.
4. Place a marker on the matching antonym, or opposite.
5. Continue playing until you make a bingo by covering five antonyms in a row. The covered row may be horizontal, vertical, or diagonal.
6. Check the words covered on the game board against the answers on the backs of the clue cards.

ANTONYM BINGO EXPERT

order	tragedy	majority	expert	loss
knowledge	pessimist	poverty	amateur	protagonist
wealth	reward	FREE	minority	comedy
optimist	civilian	ignorance	chaos	punishment
foe	military	ally	profit	antagonist

ANTONYM BINGO EXPERT

order	minority	reward	civilian	optimist
ignorance	profit	chaos	loss	foe
amateur	punishment	FREE	wealth	comedy
majority	poverty	tragedy	military	protagonist
antagonist	ally	pessimist	expert	knowledge

the opposite of **wealth**	the opposite of **chaos**	the opposite of **expert**
the opposite of **optimist**	the opposite of **ally**	the opposite of **comedy**
the opposite of **majority**	the opposite of **reward**	the opposite of **civilian**
the opposite of **knowledge**	the opposite of **profit**	the opposite of **protagonist**

amateur

Antonym Expert
EMC 3352 • © Evan-Moor Corp.

order

Antonym Expert
EMC 3352 • © Evan-Moor Corp.

poverty

Antonym Expert
EMC 3352 • © Evan-Moor Corp.

tragedy

Antonym Expert
EMC 3352 • © Evan-Moor Corp.

foe

Antonym Expert
EMC 3352 • © Evan-Moor Corp.

pessimist

Antonym Expert
EMC 3352 • © Evan-Moor Corp.

military

Antonym Expert
EMC 3352 • © Evan-Moor Corp.

punishment

Antonym Expert
EMC 3352 • © Evan-Moor Corp.

minority

Antonym Expert
EMC 3352 • © Evan-Moor Corp.

antagonist

Antonym Expert
EMC 3352 • © Evan-Moor Corp.

loss

Antonym Expert
EMC 3352 • © Evan-Moor Corp.

ignorance

Antonym Expert
EMC 3352 • © Evan-Moor Corp.

the opposite of **poverty**	the opposite of **order**	the opposite of **amateur**
the opposite of **pessimist**	the opposite of **foe**	the opposite of **tragedy**
the opposite of **minority**	the opposite of **punishment**	the opposite of **military**
the opposite of **ignorance**	the opposite of **loss**	the opposite of **antagonist**

expert

Antonym Expert

EMC 3352 • © Evan-Moor Corp.

chaos

Antonym Expert

EMC 3352 • © Evan-Moor Corp.

wealth

Antonym Expert

EMC 3352 • © Evan-Moor Corp.

comedy

Antonym Expert

EMC 3352 • © Evan-Moor Corp.

ally

Antonym Expert

EMC 3352 • © Evan-Moor Corp.

optimist

Antonym Expert

EMC 3352 • © Evan-Moor Corp.

civilian

Antonym Expert

EMC 3352 • © Evan-Moor Corp.

reward

Antonym Expert

EMC 3352 • © Evan-Moor Corp.

majority

Antonym Expert

EMC 3352 • © Evan-Moor Corp.

protagonist

Antonym Expert

EMC 3352 • © Evan-Moor Corp.

profit

Antonym Expert

EMC 3352 • © Evan-Moor Corp.

knowledge

Antonym Expert

EMC 3352 • © Evan-Moor Corp.

Answer Key

Lift the flap to check your answers.

Antonym Expert

1. poverty
2. comedy
3. foes allies
4. majority
5. protagonist
6. antagonist
7. knowledge
8. punishment
9. military
10. profit
11. chaos

Homophone Play

Preparing the Center

1. Prepare a folder following the directions on page 3.

   Cover—page 39

   Student Directions—page 41

   Game Rules—page 43

   Playing Cards—pages 45–51

   Answer Key—page 53

2. Reproduce a supply of the activity sheet on page 38. Place copies in the left-hand pocket of the folder.

Partner Practice

1. The students read the game rules for two players. The homophone card game is similar to the game Old Maid.
2. The students play Muscle Mussel. Encourage the students to read aloud each pair of sentences that they match.
3. Then the students work cooperatively to complete their own activity sheet.
4. Finally, the students check their work using the answer key.

Independent Practice

1. The student reads the game rules for one player. The homophone card game is similar to the game Concentration.
2. The student plays Muscle Mussel. After each match, the student reads aloud the homophone pair and their sentences.
3. Then the student completes the activity sheet.
4. Finally, the student self-checks by using the answer key.

Name ______________________________ **Activity Sheet**

Homophone Play

Write the matching homophones on the lines.

1. coop (○)(○) ___ ___ ___
2. principal ___ ___ ___ ___ ___ ___ (○) ___ ___
3. kernel ___ (○) ___ (○) ___ ___ ___
4. gate ___ ___ ___ ___
5. flare ___ ___ ___ ___ ___
6. mussel ___ (○) ___ ___ ___ ___
7. click (○) ___ ___ ___ ___ ___
8. Capitol ___ ___ (○) ___ ___ ___ ___
9. carol ___ ___ ___ ___ (○) ___
10. corps ___ ___ ___ ___
11. cymbal ___ ___ ___ ___ ___ ___

Unscramble the circled letters to answer the riddle below.

What do you call a two-door chicken pen on wheels?

a ___ ___ ___ ___ ___ ___ ___ ___ ___

Take It to Your Seat—Vocabulary Centers • EMC 3352 • © Evan-Moor Corp.

HOMOPHONE PLAY

"MUSCLE/MUSSEL"

Homophone Play

Student Directions

Word Wiz

Homophones are two words that sound alike but have different spellings and different meanings.

Muscle and mussel are homophones.

A **muscle** is a tissue that helps the body move.

A **mussel** is a shellfish with two hinged shells.

Follow These Steps

Partner Practice

1. Take turns reading the game rules for two players.
2. Play Muscle Mussel.
3. Work together to complete your own activity sheet.
4. Check your work using the answer key.

Independent Practice

1. Read the game rules for one player.
2. Play Muscle Mussel.
3. Complete the activity sheet.
4. Check your work using the answer key.

Rules for 2 Players:

Muscle Mussel is played like the game Old Maid.

1. Choose a dealer. The dealer shuffles the cards. The dealer deals one card at a time to both players until all the cards are dealt.
2. Place all of your matching homophone pairs faceup on the table.
3. Let the dealer choose a card from the other player. If it matches a card in the dealer's hand, the dealer places the homophone pair faceup on the table. If the card does not make a pair, the dealer holds on to it.
4. Let the second player choose a card from the dealer.
5. Continue the game until all homophone pairs have been matched. The player left with the Muscle Mussel card loses.
6. Read your homophone pairs and their sentences to each other.

Rules for 1 Player:

This version of Muscle Mussel is played like the game Concentration.

1. Set aside the Muscle Mussel card. Shuffle the rest of the cards.
2. Spread out the 22 cards facedown in rows. The cards should be close together but not overlap.
3. Select two cards and turn them faceup. If the cards are matching homophones, set them aside. If the two cards do not match, turn them over and try again.
4. Read aloud the words and sentences in the pair each time you make a match.
5. Play until you have matched all 11 pairs of homophones.

muscle

Matt liked to show off each **muscle** in his arms.

mussel

The shell of a freshwater **mussel** is often used to make buttons.

colonel

Colonel Williams stood at attention and gave orders to his troops.

kernel

It's hard to eat just one **kernel** of popcorn.

capital

Washington, D.C., is the **capital** of the United States.

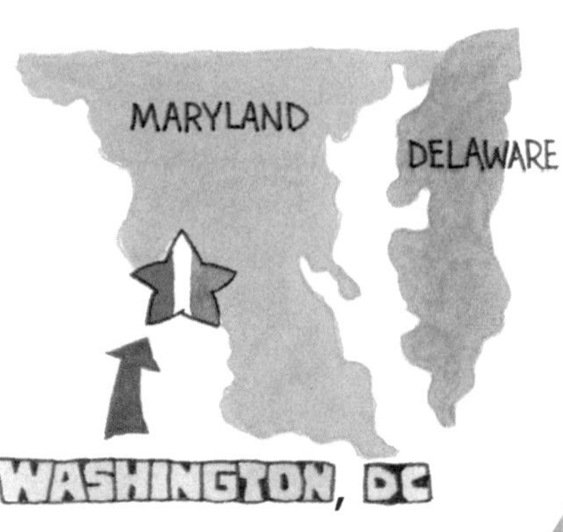

Capitol

The building in which the U.S. Congress meets is called the **Capitol**.

Homophone Play

EMC 3352 • © Evan-Moor Corp.

Homophone Play

EMC 3352 • © Evan-Moor Corp.

Homophone Play

EMC 3352 • © Evan-Moor Corp.

Homophone Play

EMC 3352 • © Evan-Moor Corp.

Homophone Play

EMC 3352 • © Evan-Moor Corp.

Homophone Play

EMC 3352 • © Evan-Moor Corp.

coop

The chicken **coop** was in need of paint and repair.

coupe

Driving a yellow **coupe** on a winding road is exciting.

click

When Joey heard the **click** of the door lock, he knew his sister Chloë didn't want to be disturbed.

clique

The three friends formed a **clique** and rudely ignored the other girls.

gate

The restless horse was ready to escape whenever the **gate** was opened.

gait

The horse's **gait** changed from a slow, steady walk to a fast gallop.

Homophone Play

EMC 3352 • © Evan-Moor Corp.

Homophone Play

EMC 3352 • © Evan-Moor Corp.

Homophone Play

EMC 3352 • © Evan-Moor Corp.

Homophone Play

EMC 3352 • © Evan-Moor Corp.

Homophone Play

EMC 3352 • © Evan-Moor Corp.

Homophone Play

EMC 3352 • © Evan-Moor Corp.

corps

The reporters in the press **corps** asked the new mayor many questions.

core

The reporters were so hungry that they ate every apple down to the **core**.

principal

I remember how to spell **principal** because the word ends in "pal" and Ms. Brown is our friend.

principle

Ms. Brown told the students that our government is based on the **principle** that all people are created equal.

carol

His proud family listened as Evan sang a beautiful Christmas **carol**.

carrel

Evan had a pile of textbooks to study in the library **carrel**.

Homophone Play

EMC 3352 • © Evan-Moor Corp.

Homophone Play

EMC 3352 • © Evan-Moor Corp.

Homophone Play

EMC 3352 • © Evan-Moor Corp.

Homophone Play

EMC 3352 • © Evan-Moor Corp.

Homophone Play

EMC 3352 • © Evan-Moor Corp.

Homophone Play

EMC 3352 • © Evan-Moor Corp.

cymbal

When Bella dropped her **cymbal,** the sharp ringing sound could be heard throughout the school.

symbol

Bella painted a dove on her instrument as a **symbol** of peace.

flare

Carlos read the scary book to his friends by the **flare** of the campfire.

flair

Carlos showed a real **flair** for storytelling.

Muscle Mussel

Homophone Play

EMC 3352 • © Evan-Moor Corp.

Homophone Play

EMC 3352 • © Evan-Moor Corp.

Homophone Play

EMC 3352 • © Evan-Moor Corp.

Homophone Play

EMC 3352 • © Evan-Moor Corp.

Homophone Play

EMC 3352 • © Evan-Moor Corp.

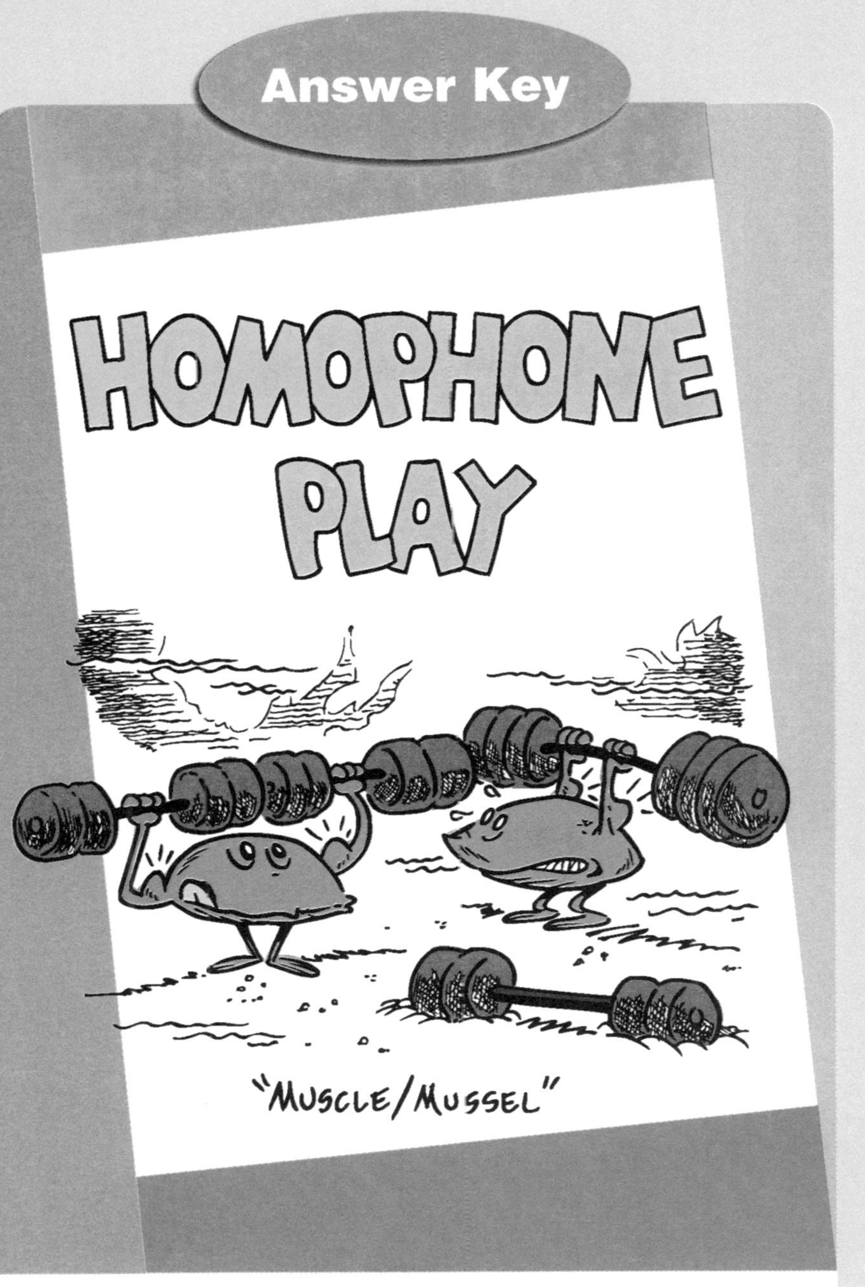

Answer Key
HOMOPHONE PLAY
"MUSCLE/MUSSEL"
Lift the flap to check your answers.

Homophone Play

1. coupe
2. principle
3. colonel
4. gait
5. flair
6. muscle
7. clique
8. capital
9. carrel
10. core
11. symbol

What do you call a two-door chicken pen on wheels?

a c o o p c o u p e

Presenting Prefixes

Preparing the Center

1. Prepare a folder following the directions on page 3.

   Cover—page 57

   Student Directions—page 59

   Puzzle Pieces—pages 61–65

   Answer Key—page 67

2. Reproduce a supply of the activity sheet on page 56. Place copies in the left-hand pocket of the folder.

Partner Practice

1. The students sort the puzzle pieces into two piles—prefixes and base words.
2. Working together, the students match a prefix and a base word to form a new word. The students take turns reading aloud the new word and defining it. The students then turn the puzzle over and read the definition and the sentence that uses the word.
3. The students repeat Step 2 to complete the other 11 puzzles.
4. Then the students work cooperatively to complete their own activity sheet.
5. Finally, the students check their work using the answer key.

Independent Practice

1. The student sorts the puzzle pieces into two piles—prefixes and base words.
2. The student matches a prefix and a base word to form a new word. The student reads aloud the new word and defines it. The student turns the puzzle over to read the definition and the sentence that uses the word.
3. The student repeats Step 2 to complete the other 11 puzzles.
4. Then the student completes the activity sheet.
5. Finally, the student self-checks by using the answer key.

Name ______________________ **Activity Sheet**

Presenting Prefixes

Write the correct prefix for each base word. Write the new word that is formed. Use each prefix two times.

Prefixes

bi—two	**il**—not	**ultra**—beyond
hyper—too much	**mid**—middle	**uni**—one

Prefix	Base Word	New Word
1. uni	form	______
2. ______	legal	______
3. ______	critical	______
4. ______	lingual	______
5. ______	violet	______
6. ______	legible	______
7. ______	annual	______
8. ______	active	______
9. ______	day	______
10. ______	corn	______
11. ______	sonic	______
12. ______	week	______

Take It to Your Seat—Vocabulary Centers • EMC 3352 • © Evan-Moor Corp.

PRESENTING PREFIXES

"UNICORN" "UNIFORM"

Presenting Prefixes

Student Directions

Word Wiz

A **prefix** is a word part that is added to the beginning of a word. When you add a prefix, you change the word's meaning.

prefix	+	base word	=	new word
bi (two)	+	annual (once a year)	=	biannual (twice a year)

Common Prefixes

bi—two	**il**—not	**ultra**—beyond
hyper—too much	**mid**—middle	**uni**—one

Follow These Steps

Partner Practice

1. Sort the puzzle pieces into two piles—prefixes and base words.
2. Working together, match the prefixes to the correct base words to form 12 new words.
3. Take turns reading aloud the new words and determining what they mean. Turn the puzzles over to read the definition and the sentence.
4. Work together to complete your own activity sheet.
5. Check your work using the answer key.

Independent Practice

1. Sort the puzzle pieces into two piles—prefixes and base words.
2. Match a prefix to the correct base word to create a new word.
3. Read aloud the new word and think about its meaning. Turn the puzzle over to read the definition and the sentence.
4. Repeat Steps 2 and 3 to form the other 11 new words.
5. Complete the activity sheet.
6. Check your work using the answer key.

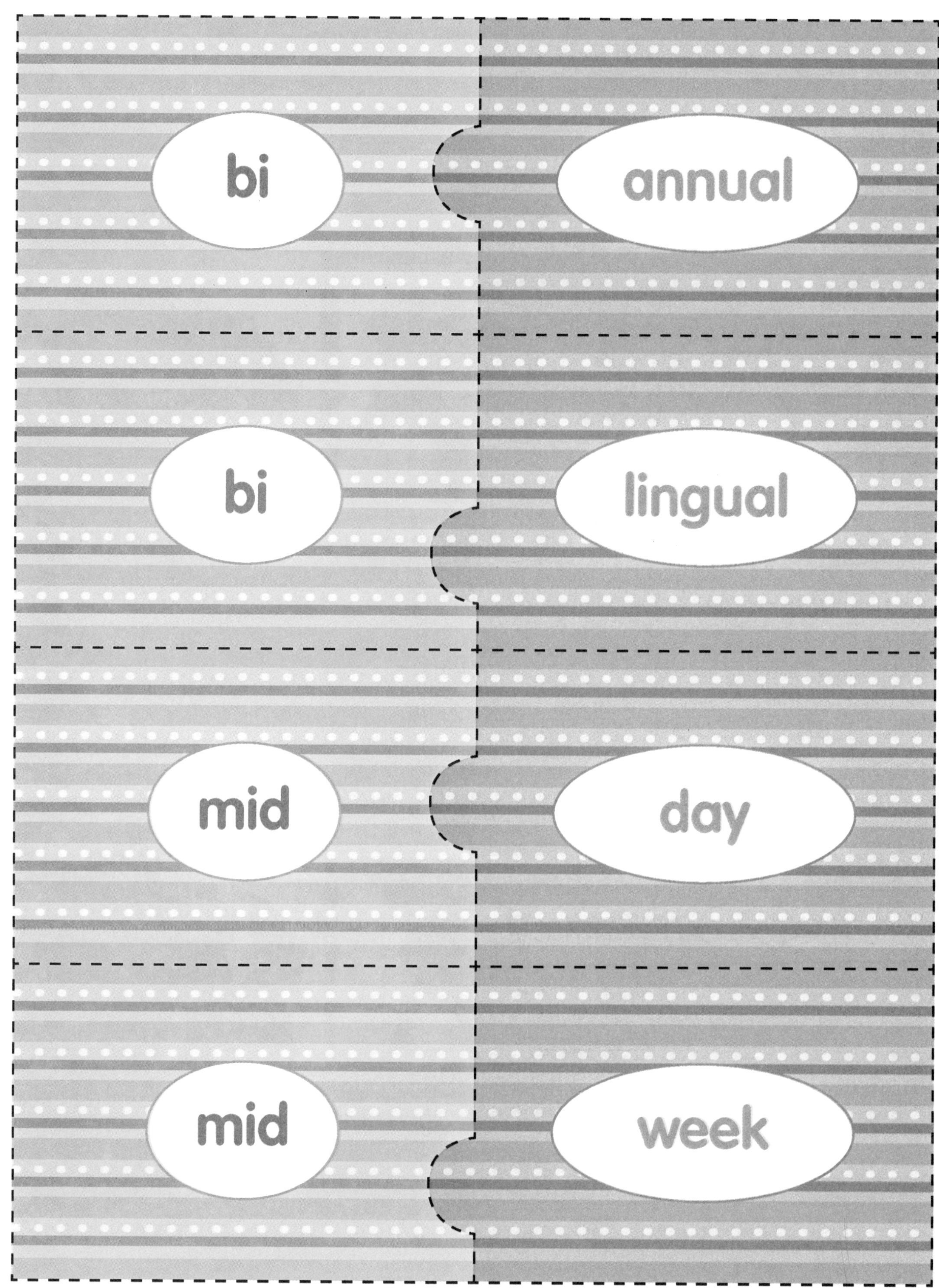
bi
annual
bi
lingual
mid
day
mid
week

biannual: twice a year

The large department store has great **biannual** sales.

Presenting Prefixes
EMC 3352 • © Evan-Moor Corp.

Presenting Prefixes
EMC 3352 • © Evan-Moor Corp.

bilingual: able to use two languages

Maya is **bilingual** and speaks both English and Spanish.

Presenting Prefixes
EMC 3352 • © Evan-Moor Corp.

Presenting Prefixes
EMC 3352 • © Evan-Moor Corp.

midday: noon, or 12 o'clock in the middle of the day

Let's meet for lunch at **midday**.

Presenting Prefixes
EMC 3352 • © Evan-Moor Corp.

Presenting Prefixes
EMC 3352 • © Evan-Moor Corp.

midweek: middle of the week

Wednesday is considered **midweek** in most offices.

Presenting Prefixes
EMC 3352 • © Evan-Moor Corp.

Presenting Prefixes
EMC 3352 • © Evan-Moor Corp.

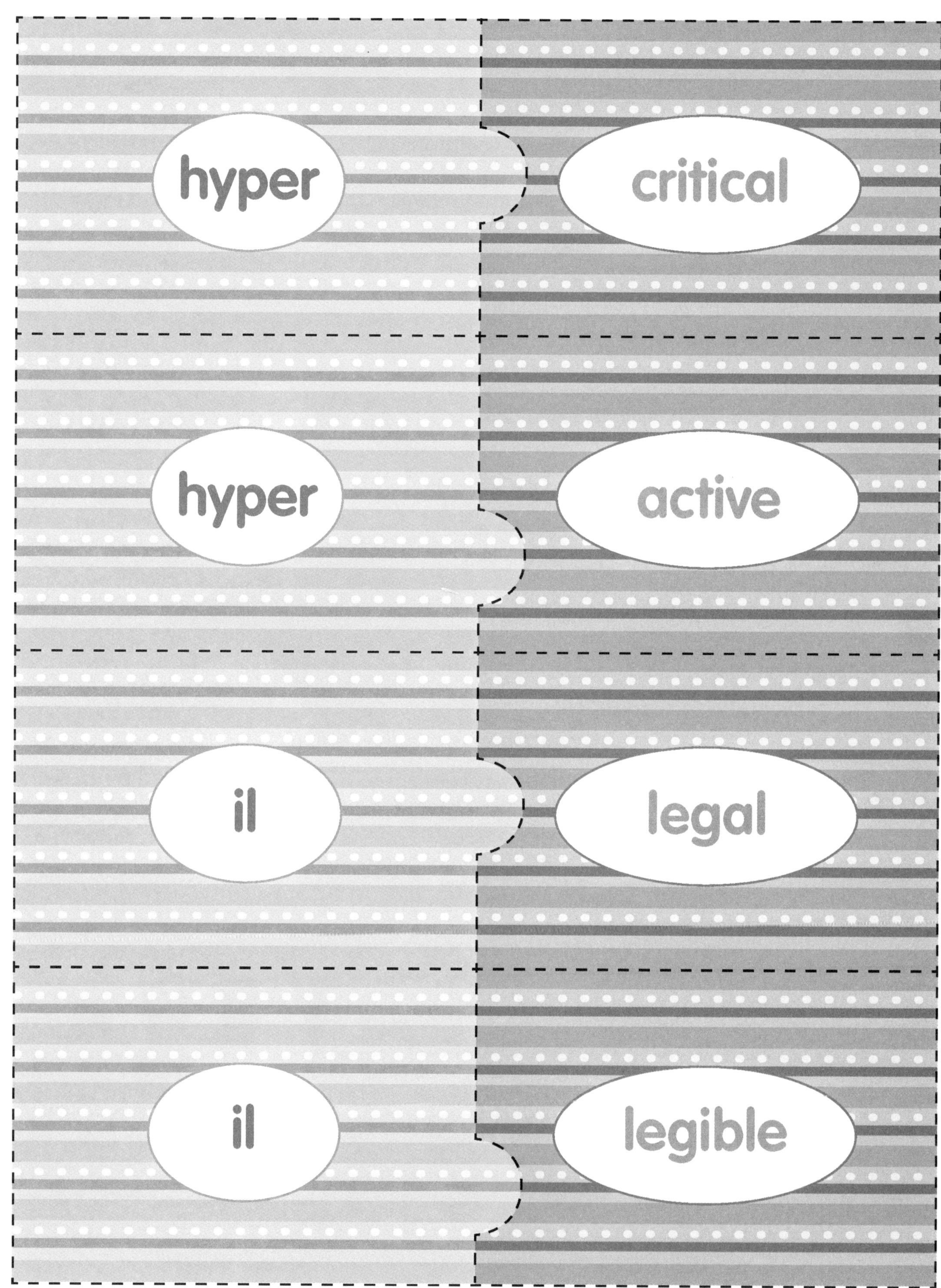
hyper
critical
hyper
active
il
legal
il
legible

hypercritical: tending to find too much fault

Andrew was **hypercritical** of his sister's friends.

Presenting Prefixes
EMC 3352 • © Evan-Moor Corp.

Presenting Prefixes
EMC 3352 • © Evan-Moor Corp.

hyperactive: too active; having difficulty sitting quietly

Megan is **hyperactive** and finds it difficult to fall asleep.

Presenting Prefixes
EMC 3352 • © Evan-Moor Corp.

Presenting Prefixes
EMC 3352 • © Evan-Moor Corp.

illegal: not lawful

It is **illegal** to drive without a license.

Presenting Prefixes
EMC 3352 • © Evan-Moor Corp.

Presenting Prefixes
EMC 3352 • © Evan-Moor Corp.

illegible: not clear enough to be read easily

I can't read Mr. Abbott's handwriting because it is **illegible**.

Presenting Prefixes
EMC 3352 • © Evan-Moor Corp.

Presenting Prefixes
EMC 3352 • © Evan-Moor Corp.

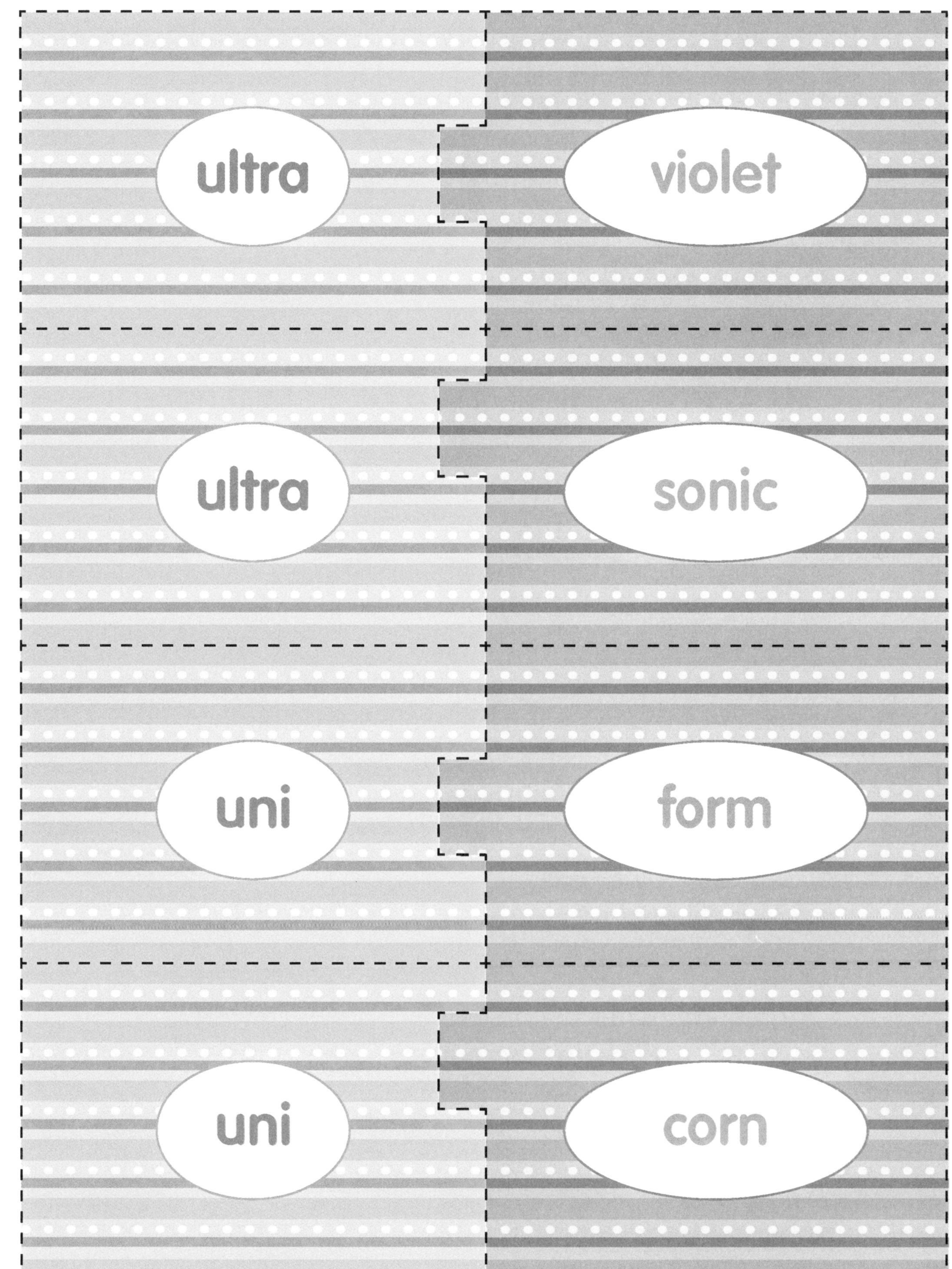
ultra
violet
ultra
sonic
uni
form
uni
corn

ultraviolet: light that is beyond violet and can't be seen

Be sure to wear sunglasses that protect your eyes from **ultraviolet** light.

Presenting Prefixes
EMC 3352 • © Evan-Moor Corp.

Presenting Prefixes
EMC 3352 • © Evan-Moor Corp

ultrasonic: sound frequency that is too high for humans to hear

Bats use **ultrasonic** calls to locate their prey.

Presenting Prefixes
EMC 3352 • © Evan-Moor Corp.

Presenting Prefixes
EMC 3352 • © Evan-Moor Corp

uniform: always the same; never changing

The jogger keeps a **uniform** pace as he runs for miles.

Presenting Prefixes
EMC 3352 • © Evan-Moor Corp.

Presenting Prefixes
EMC 3352 • © Evan-Moor Corp

unicorn: mythical horse-like creature that has one horn growing out of its forehead

The myth of the **unicorn** has lasted for thousands of years.

Presenting Prefixes
EMC 3352 • © Evan-Moor Corp.

Presenting Prefixes
EMC 3352 • © Evan-Moor Corp

Answer Key

Lift the flap to check your answers.

Presenting Prefixes

	Prefix	Base Word	New Word
1.	uni	form	uniform
2.	il	legal	illegal
3.	hyper	critical	hypercritical
4.	bi	lingual	bilingual
5.	ultra	violet	ultraviolet
6.	il	legible	illegible
7.	bi	annual	biannual
8.	hyper	active	hyperactive
9.	mid	day	midday
10.	uni	corn	unicorn
11.	ultra	sonic	ultrasonic
12.	mid	week	midweek

All About Acronyms

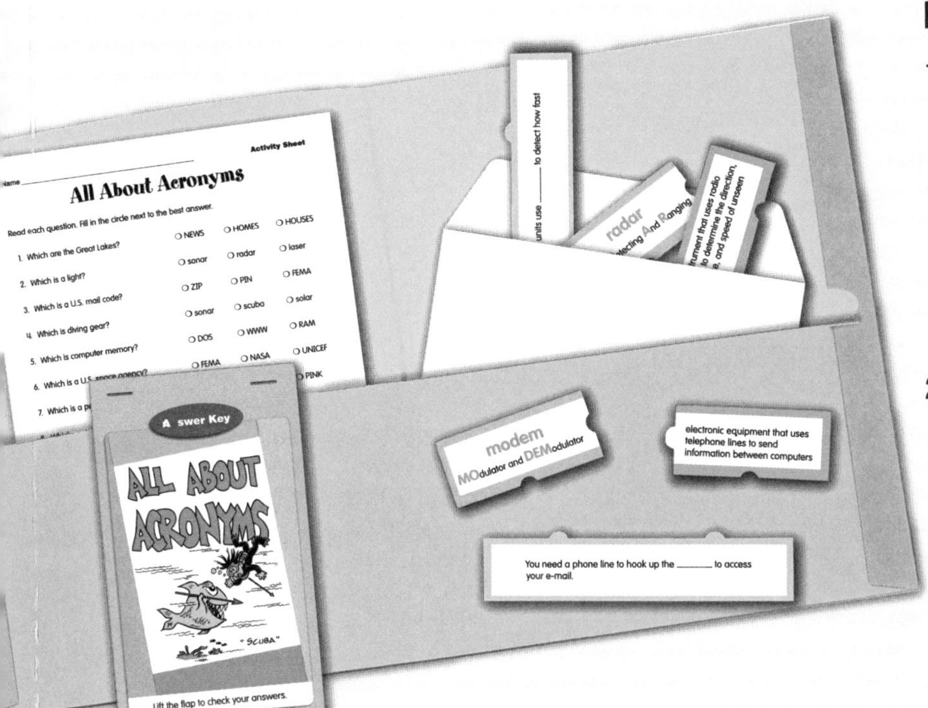

Preparing the Center

1. Prepare a folder following the directions on page 3.

   Cover—page 71

   Student Directions—page 73

   Puzzle Pieces—pages 75–81

   Answer Key—page 83

2. Reproduce a supply of the activity sheet on page 70. Place copies in the left-hand pocket of the folder.

Partner Practice

1. The students sort the puzzle pieces into three piles—acronyms, their explanations, and sentences.
2. Working together, the students choose an acronym. They match the acronym to its explanation and sentence by using context clues.
3. The students repeat Step 2 to complete the remaining 11 puzzles.
4. Then the students work cooperatively to complete their own activity sheet.
5. Finally, the students check their work using the answer key.

Independent Practice

1. The student sorts the puzzle pieces into three piles—acronyms, their explanations, and sentences.
2. The student chooses an acronym. The student matches the acronym to its explanation and sentence by using context clues.
3. The student repeats Step 2 to complete the remaining 11 puzzles.
4. Then the student completes the activity sheet.
5. Finally, the student self-checks by using the answer key.

Name ____________________ **Activity Sheet**

All About Acronyms

Read each question. Fill in the circle next to the correct answer.

1. Which are the Great Lakes?	❍ NEWS	❍ HOMES	❍ HOUSES
2. Which is a light?	❍ sonar	❍ radar	❍ laser
3. Which is a U.S. mail code?	❍ ZIP	❍ PIN	❍ FEMA
4. Which is diving gear?	❍ sonar	❍ scuba	❍ solar
5. Which is computer memory?	❍ DOS	❍ WWW	❍ RAM
6. Which is a U.S. space agency?	❍ FEMA	❍ NASA	❍ UNICEF
7. Which is a personal ID?	❍ PIN	❍ PID	❍ PINK
8. Which pertains to sound waves?	❍ radar	❍ laser	❍ sonar
9. Which is a volunteer agency?	❍ NASA	❍ VISTA	❍ FEMA
10. Which works with disasters?	❍ HOMES	❍ FEMA	❍ ZIP
11. Which operates with telephone lines?	❍ scuba	❍ RAM	❍ modem
12. Which pertains to radio waves?	❍ radar	❍ sonar	❍ scuba

ALL ABOUT ACRONYMS

"SCUBA"

All About Acronyms

Student Directions

Word Wiz

An **acronym** is a word made from the first or first few letters of the words in a phrase. Acronyms do not have periods between the letters.

radar

is an acronym for the words

RAdio **D**etecting **A**nd **R**anging

Follow These Steps

Partner Practice

1. Sort the puzzle pieces into three piles—acronyms, their explanations, and sentences.
2. Match an acronym and its explanation to the corresponding sentence. Take turns reading aloud the completed puzzle.
3. Repeat Step 2 to complete the other 11 puzzles.
4. Then work together to complete your own activity sheet.
5. Check your work using the answer key.

Independent Practice

1. Sort the puzzle pieces into three piles—acronyms, their explanations, and sentences.
2. Match an acronym to its explanation and the corresponding sentence to form a three-piece puzzle. Read aloud the puzzle.
3. Repeat Step 2 to complete the other 11 puzzles.
4. Complete the activity sheet.
5. Check your work using the answer key.

modem

MOdulator and **DEM**odulator

electronic equipment that uses telephone lines to send information between computers

You need a phone line to hook up the _______ to access your e-mail.

radar

RAdio **D**etecting **A**nd **R**anging

an instrument that uses radio waves to determine the direction, distance, and speed of unseen objects

Some highway patrol units use _______ to detect how fast a car is going.

PIN

Personal **I**dentification **N**umber

a person's identification number that's entered on a keypad to access an account

Emma typed her four-digit _______ to withdraw money from her checking account.

All About Acronyms

EMC 3352 • © Evan-Moor Corp.

All About Acronyms

EMC 3352 • © Evan-Moor Corp.

All About Acronyms

EMC 3352 • © Evan-Moor Corp.

All About Acronyms

EMC 3352 • © Evan-Moor Corp.

All About Acronyms

EMC 3352 • © Evan-Moor Corp.

All About Acronyms

EMC 3352 • © Evan-Moor Corp.

All About Acronyms

EMC 3352 • © Evan-Moor Corp.

All About Acronyms

EMC 3352 • © Evan-Moor Corp.

All About Acronyms

EMC 3352 • © Evan-Moor Corp.

ZIP

Zone Improvement Plan

a code used to organize mail delivery

All the postal service ________ codes in California start with the numeral nine.

scuba

Self-Contained Underwater Breathing Apparatus

the gear that helps a diver breathe underwater

Marine biologists wear an air tank, face mask, wet suit, and other ________ equipment while they explore underwater plants.

sonar

SOund Navigation And Ranging

a device that uses sound waves to locate objects that are underwater

Dolphins use a natural ________ system to detect underwater things in their path.

All About Acronyms

EMC 3352 • © Evan-Moor Corp.

All About Acronyms

EMC 3352 • © Evan-Moor Corp.

All About Acronyms

EMC 3352 • © Evan-Moor Corp.

All About Acronyms

EMC 3352 • © Evan-Moor Corp.

All About Acronyms

EMC 3352 • © Evan-Moor Corp.

All About Acronyms

EMC 3352 • © Evan-Moor Corp.

All About Acronyms

EMC 3352 • © Evan-Moor Corp.

All About Acronyms

EMC 3352 • © Evan-Moor Corp.

All About Acronyms

EMC 3352 • © Evan-Moor Corp.

NASA

National **A**eronautics and **S**pace **A**dministration

the United States' space agency

In 1958, ________ launched its first satellite, *Explorer 1*.

laser

Light **A**mplification by **S**timulated **E**mission of **R**adiation

a device that makes a very narrow, powerful beam of light

________ beams are used to read compact discs.

HOMES

Huron, **O**ntario, **M**ichigan, **E**rie, **S**uperior

an acronym for memorizing the Great Lakes of the United States

When asked to name the Great Lakes, Brad used the acronym ________ to recall all five.

All About Acronyms

EMC 3352 • © Evan-Moor Corp.

All About Acronyms

EMC 3352 • © Evan-Moor Corp.

All About Acronyms

EMC 3352 • © Evan-Moor Corp.

All About Acronyms

EMC 3352 • © Evan-Moor Corp.

All About Acronyms

EMC 3352 • © Evan-Moor Corp.

All About Acronyms

EMC 3352 • © Evan-Moor Corp.

All About Acronyms

EMC 3352 • © Evan-Moor Corp.

All About Acronyms

EMC 3352 • © Evan-Moor Corp.

All About Acronyms

EMC 3352 • © Evan-Moor Corp.

FEMA

Federal Emergency Management Agency

an organization within the federal government that helps people prepare for disasters and helps give relief when disasters strike

After the earthquake toppled the city, representatives from ________ helped the homeless find shelter.

VISTA

Volunteers In Service To America

an organization of people who offer to help the needy for little pay

Upon graduating from college, Ahmed joined ________ and helped people form community vegetable gardens.

RAM

Random-Access Memory

the memory a computer uses to open programs and store work until it's saved

Your computer's ________ lets you access information very quickly.

All About Acronyms
EMC 3352 • © Evan-Moor Corp.

All About Acronyms
EMC 3352 • © Evan-Moor Corp.

All About Acronyms
EMC 3352 • © Evan-Moor Corp.

All About Acronyms
EMC 3352 • © Evan-Moor Corp.

All About Acronyms
EMC 3352 • © Evan-Moor Corp.

All About Acronyms
EMC 3352 • © Evan-Moor Corp.

All About Acronyms
EMC 3352 • © Evan-Moor Corp.

All About Acronyms
EMC 3352 • © Evan-Moor Corp.

All About Acronyms
EMC 3352 • © Evan-Moor Corp.

Answer Key

ALL ABOUT ACRONYMS

"SCUBA"

Lift the flap to check your answers.

All About Acronyms

1. HOMES
2. laser
3. ZIP
4. scuba
5. RAM
6. NASA
7. PIN
8. sonar
9. VISTA
10. FEMA
11. modem
12. radar

Analyzing Analogies

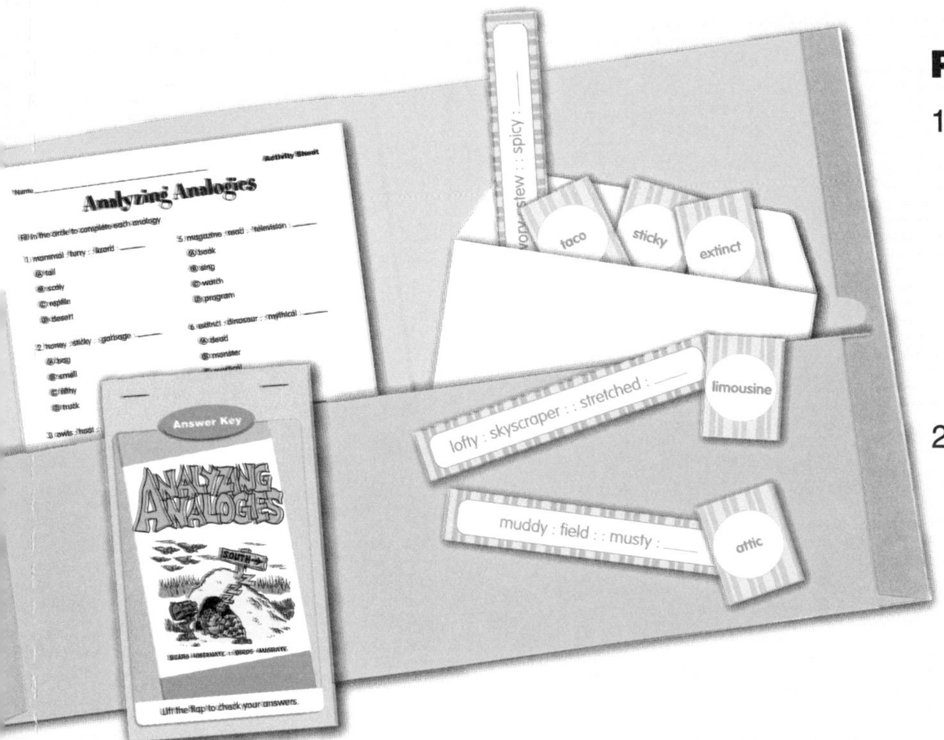

Preparing the Center

1. Prepare a folder following the directions on page 3.

   Cover—page 87

   Student Directions—page 89

   Task Cards—pages 91–95

   Answer Key—page 97

2. Reproduce a supply of the activity sheet on page 86. Place copies in the left-hand pocket of the folder.

Partner Practice

1. The students sort the task cards into two piles—analogy starters and words. The students will practice two kinds of analogies—*object : action* and *object : description.*
2. Working together, the students read an analogy starter and find the word that completes it. They turn the cards over to self-check.
3. The students repeat Step 2 to complete the other 15 analogies.
4. Then the students work cooperatively to complete their own activity sheet.
5. Finally, the students check their work using the answer key.

Independent Practice

1. The student sorts the task cards into two piles—analogy starters and words. The student will practice two kinds of analogies—*object : action* and *object : description.*
2. The student reads an analogy starter and finds the word that completes it. The student turns the cards over to self-check.
3. The student repeats Step 2 to complete the other 15 analogies.
4. Then the student completes the activity sheet.
5. Finally, the student self-checks by using the answer key.

Name ____________________ **Activity Sheet**

Analyzing Analogies

Fill in the circle to complete each analogy.

1. mammal : furry : : lizard : ______
   - Ⓐ tail
   - Ⓑ scaly
   - Ⓒ reptile
   - Ⓓ desert

2. honey : sticky : : garbage : ______
   - Ⓐ bag
   - Ⓑ smell
   - Ⓒ filthy
   - Ⓓ truck

3. owls : hoot : : prairie dogs : ______
   - Ⓐ live
   - Ⓑ bark
   - Ⓒ colonies
   - Ⓓ underground

4. fingernails : polish : : wood : ______
   - Ⓐ dark
   - Ⓑ hard
   - Ⓒ lumber
   - Ⓓ varnish

5. magazine : read : : television : ______
   - Ⓐ book
   - Ⓑ sing
   - Ⓒ watch
   - Ⓓ program

6. extinct : dinosaur : : mythical : ______
   - Ⓐ dead
   - Ⓑ monster
   - Ⓒ mystical
   - Ⓓ imaginary

7. bears : hibernate : : birds : ______
   - Ⓐ wings
   - Ⓑ feathers
   - Ⓒ migrate
   - Ⓓ chirp

8. attic : musty : : field : ______
   - Ⓐ muddy
   - Ⓑ meadow
   - Ⓒ grass
   - Ⓓ mouse

ANALYZING ANALOGIES

BEARS : HIBERNATE :: BIRDS : MIGRATE

Analyzing Analogies

Student Directions

An **analogy** is a comparison that shows the relationship between two pairs of words.

Two Kinds of Analogies

1

An Object and An Action
fence : paint : : car : wax
(**fence** is to **paint** as **car** is to **wax**)
or
An Action and An Object
paint : fence : : wax : car
(**paint** is to **fence** as **wax** is to **car**)

2

An Object and Its Description
apple : red : : banana : yellow
(**apple** is to **red** as **banana** is to **yellow**)
or
A Description and An Object
red : apple : : yellow : banana
(**red** is to **apple** as **yellow** is to **banana**)

Follow These Steps

Partner Practice

1. Sort the cards into two piles—analogy starters and word cards.
2. Read an analogy starter. Find the word card that completes the analogy. Take turns reading the analogy to each other. Turn the two cards over to check your work.
3. Repeat Step 2 to complete the other 15 analogies.
4. Work together to complete your own activity sheet.
5. Check your work using the answer key.

Independent Practice

1. Sort the cards into two piles—analogy starters and word cards.
2. Read an analogy starter. Find the word card that completes the analogy. Read the analogy aloud. Turn the two cards over to check your work.
3. Repeat Step 2 to complete the other 15 analogies.
4. Complete the activity sheet.
5. Check your work using the answer key.

lofty : skyscraper : : stretched : ____

muddy : field : : musty : ____

savory : stew : : spicy : ____

scorching : desert : : frigid : ____

mammal : furry : : lizard : ____

monster : mythical : : dinosaur : ____

skiis : straight : : boomerangs : ____

garbage : filthy : : honey : ____

Analyzing Analogies

EMC 3352 • © Evan-Moor Corp.

Analyzing Analogies

EMC 3352 • © Evan-Moor Corp.

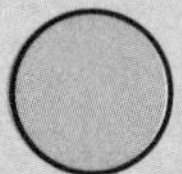

Analyzing Analogies

EMC 3352 • © Evan-Moor Corp.

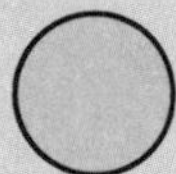

Analyzing Analogies

EMC 3352 • © Evan-Moor Corp.

Analyzing Analogies

EMC 3352 • © Evan-Moor Corp.

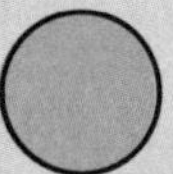

Analyzing Analogies

EMC 3352 • © Evan-Moor Corp.

Analyzing Analogies

EMC 3352 • © Evan-Moor Corp.

Analyzing Analogies

EMC 3352 • © Evan-Moor Corp.

mountain : climb : : lake : ____

cats : meow : : lions : ____

open : book : : peel : ____

birds : migrate : : bears : ____

varnish : wood : : polish : ____

bark : prairie dogs : : hoot : ____

read : magazine : : watch : ____

play : saxophone : : strum : ____

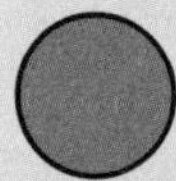

Analyzing Analogies

EMC 3352 • © Evan-Moor Corp.

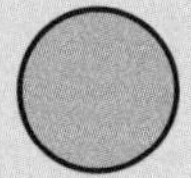

Analyzing Analogies

EMC 3352 • © Evan-Moor Corp.

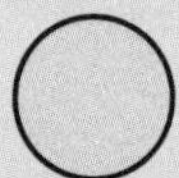

Analyzing Analogies

EMC 3352 • © Evan-Moor Corp.

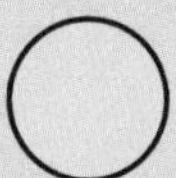

Analyzing Analogies

EMC 3352 • © Evan-Moor Corp.

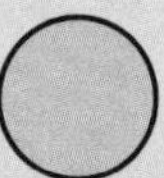

Analyzing Analogies

EMC 3352 • © Evan-Moor Corp.

Analyzing Analogies

EMC 3352 • © Evan-Moor Corp.

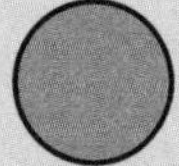

Analyzing Analogies

EMC 3352 • © Evan-Moor Corp.

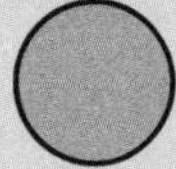

Analyzing Analogies

EMC 3352 • © Evan-Moor Corp.

limousine	attic	taco	tundra
scaly	extinct	curved	sticky
swim	roar	banana	hibernate
fingernails	owls	television	guitar

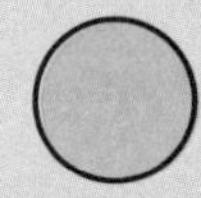

Analyzing Analogies

EMC 3352

© Evan-Moor Corp.

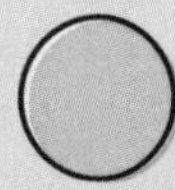

Analyzing Analogies

EMC 3352

© Evan-Moor Corp.

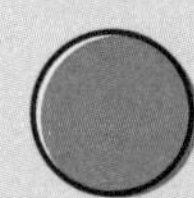

Analyzing Analogies

EMC 3352

© Evan-Moor Corp.

Analyzing Analogies

EMC 3352

© Evan-Moor Corp.

Analyzing Analogies

EMC 3352

© Evan-Moor Corp.

Analyzing Analogies

EMC 3352

© Evan-Moor Corp.

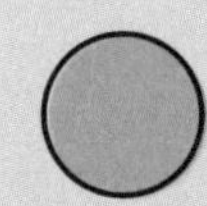

Analyzing Analogies

EMC 3352

© Evan-Moor Corp.

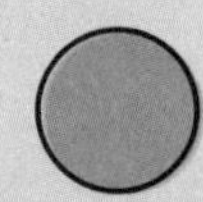

Analyzing Analogies

EMC 3352

© Evan-Moor Corp.

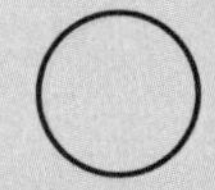

Analyzing Analogies

EMC 3352

© Evan-Moor Corp.

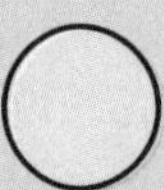

Analyzing Analogies

EMC 3352

© Evan-Moor Corp.

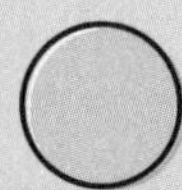

Analyzing Analogies

EMC 3352

© Evan-Moor Corp.

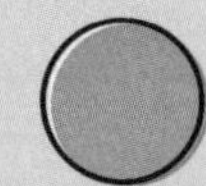

Analyzing Analogies

EMC 3352

© Evan-Moor Corp.

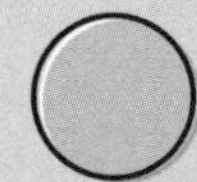

Analyzing Analogies

EMC 3352

© Evan-Moor Corp.

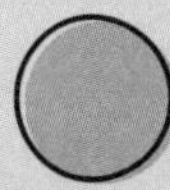

Analyzing Analogies

EMC 3352

© Evan-Moor Corp.

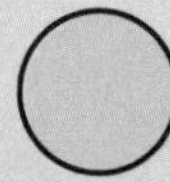

Analyzing Analogies

EMC 3352

© Evan-Moor Corp.

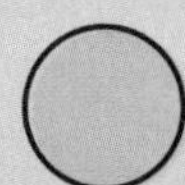

Analyzing Analogies

EMC 3352

© Evan-Moor Corp.

Answer Key

ANALYZING ANALOGIES

SOUTH →

B.BEAR

BEARS : HIBERNATE :: BIRDS : MIGRATE

Lift the flap to check your answers.

Analyzing Analogies

1. B—scaly
2. C—filthy
3. B—bark
4. D—varnish
5. C—watch
6. B—monster
7. C—migrate
8. A—muddy

Dramatic Compounds

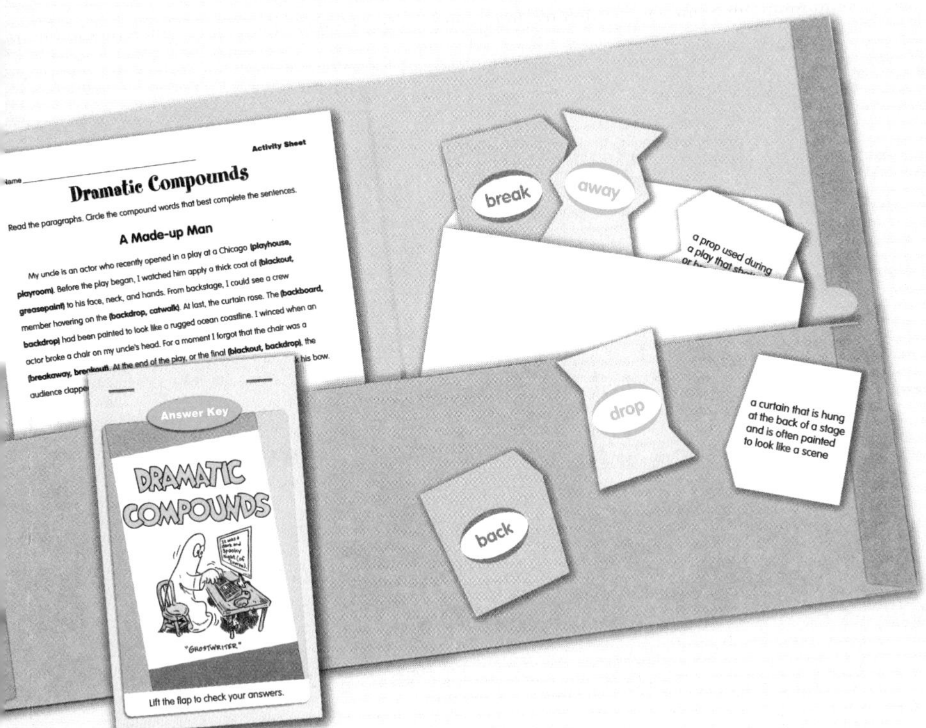

Preparing the Center

1. Prepare a folder following the directions on page 3.

   Cover—page 101

   Student Directions—page 103

   Puzzle Pieces—pages 105–111

   Answer Key—page 113
2. Reproduce a supply of the activity sheet on page 100. Place copies in the left-hand pocket of the folder.

Partner Practice

1. The students sort the puzzle pieces into three piles—pink words, green words, and definitions.
2. Working together, the students match a pink word and a green word to form a dramatic compound word, and then match that compound to its definition.
3. The students repeat Step 2 to complete the other 11 puzzles. Encourage the students to read aloud each compound word and its definition.
4. Then the students work cooperatively to complete their own activity sheet.
5. Finally, the students check their work using the answer key.

Independent Practice

1. The student sorts the puzzle pieces into three piles—pink words, green words, and definitions.
2. The student matches a pink word and a green word to form a dramatic compound word, and then matches that compound to its definition.
3. The student repeats Step 2 to complete the other 11 puzzles. Encourage the student to read aloud each compound word and its definition.
4. Then the student completes the activity sheet.
5. Finally, the student self-checks by using the answer key.

Name ____________________ **Activity Sheet**

Dramatic Compounds

Read the paragraphs. Circle the compound words that best complete the sentences.

A Made-up Man

My uncle is an actor who recently opened in a play at a Chicago **(playhouse, playroom)**. Before the play began, I watched him apply a thick coat of **(blackout, greasepaint)** to his face, neck, and hands. From backstage, I could see a crew member hovering on the **(backdrop, catwalk)**. At last, the curtain rose. The **(backboard, backdrop)** had been painted to look like a rugged ocean coastline. I winced when an actor broke a chair on my uncle's head. For a moment, I forgot that the chair was a **(breakaway, breakout)**. At the end of the play, or the final **(blackout, backdrop)**, the audience clapped enthusiastically. My uncle looked right at me before he took his bow.

Born to Write

Zora Neale Hurston, a renowned African-American writer, had a gift for storytelling. The talented Hurston did not depend on a **(pen name, ghostwriter)** to write for her. One of her novels was so well-written, it's considered a **(masterpiece, viewpoint)**. A popular Hurston novel is told from the **(copyright, viewpoint)** of a young black woman. On occasion, Hurston used the **(flashback, flash-forward)** technique. She went from present actions to past actions and back again. Zora spent years collecting and writing down the rich **(folklore, flashback)** of the black South. Her autobiography has a **(masterpiece, copyright)** date of 1942. Nearly 50 years after her death, Hurston's books about the African-American culture continue to inspire and inform.

DRAMATIC COMPOUNDS

"GHOSTWRITER"

Dramatic Compounds

Student Directions

Word Wiz

A compound word is a word made up of two words put together.

The two words black and out are combined to make the compound word blackout.

Follow These Steps

Partner Practice

1. Sort the puzzle pieces into three piles—pink words, green words, and definitions.
2. Match a pink word and a green word to form a compound word. Match that compound word to its definition to make a three-part puzzle.
3. Complete the other 11 puzzles. Read each compound word and its definition aloud.
4. Work together to complete your own activity sheet.
5. Check your work using the answer key.

Independent Practice

1. Sort the puzzle pieces into three piles—pink words, green words, and definitions.
2. Match a pink word and a green word to form a compound word. Match that compound word to its definition to make a three-part puzzle.
3. Complete the other 11 puzzles. Read each compound word and its definition aloud.
4. Complete the activity sheet.
5. Check your work using the answer key.

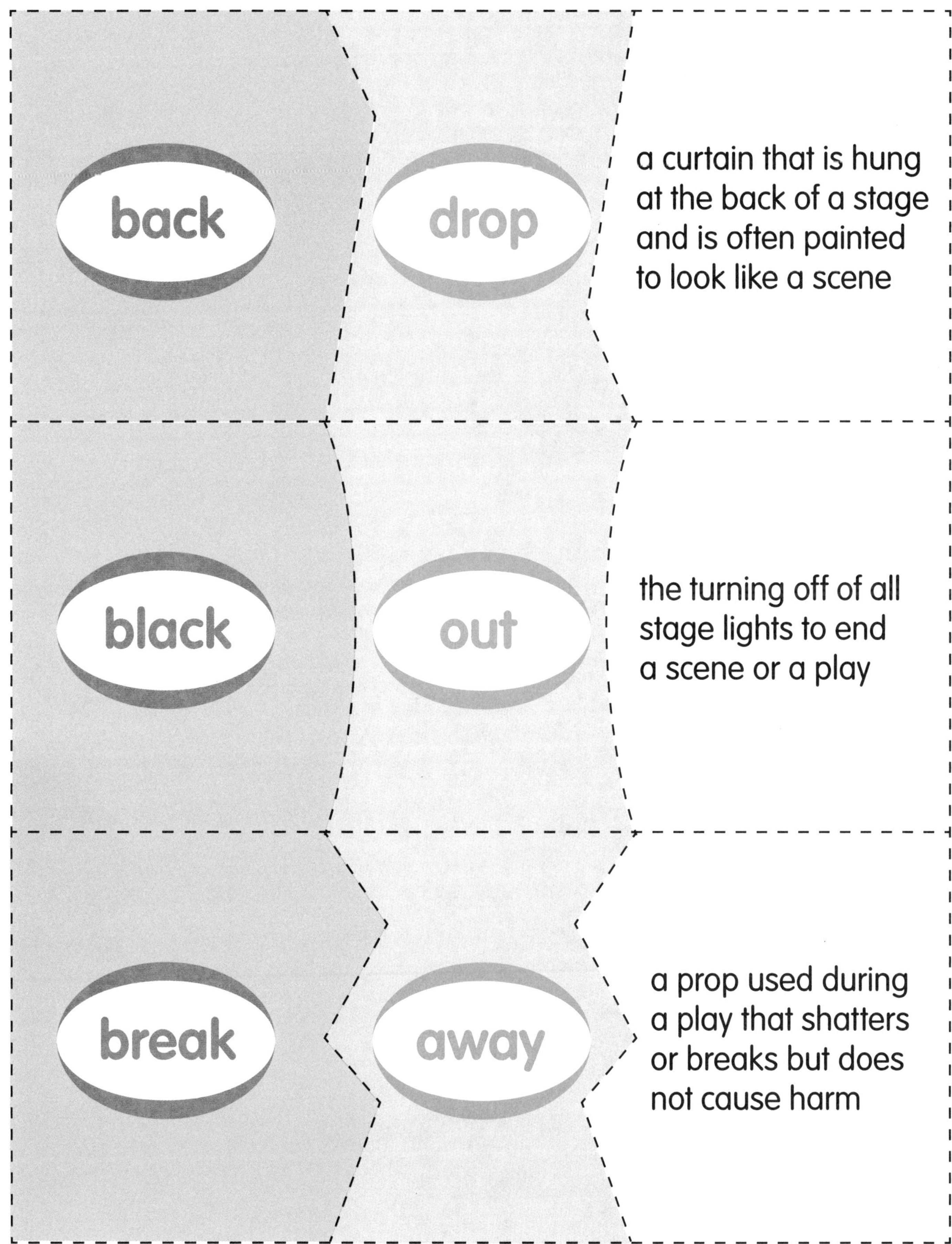
back
drop
a curtain that is hung at the back of a stage and is often painted to look like a scene
black
out
the turning off of all stage lights to end a scene or a play
break
away
a prop used during a play that shatters or breaks but does not cause harm

Dramatic Compounds

EMC 3352
© Evan-Moor Corp.

Dramatic Compounds

EMC 3352
© Evan-Moor Corp.

Dramatic Compounds

EMC 3352
© Evan-Moor Corp.

Dramatic Compounds

EMC 3352
© Evan-Moor Corp.

Dramatic Compounds

EMC 3352
© Evan-Moor Corp.

Dramatic Compounds

EMC 3352
© Evan-Moor Corp.

Dramatic Compounds

EMC 3352
© Evan-Moor Corp.

Dramatic Compounds

EMC 3352
© Evan-Moor Corp.

Dramatic Compounds

EMC 3352
© Evan-Moor Corp.

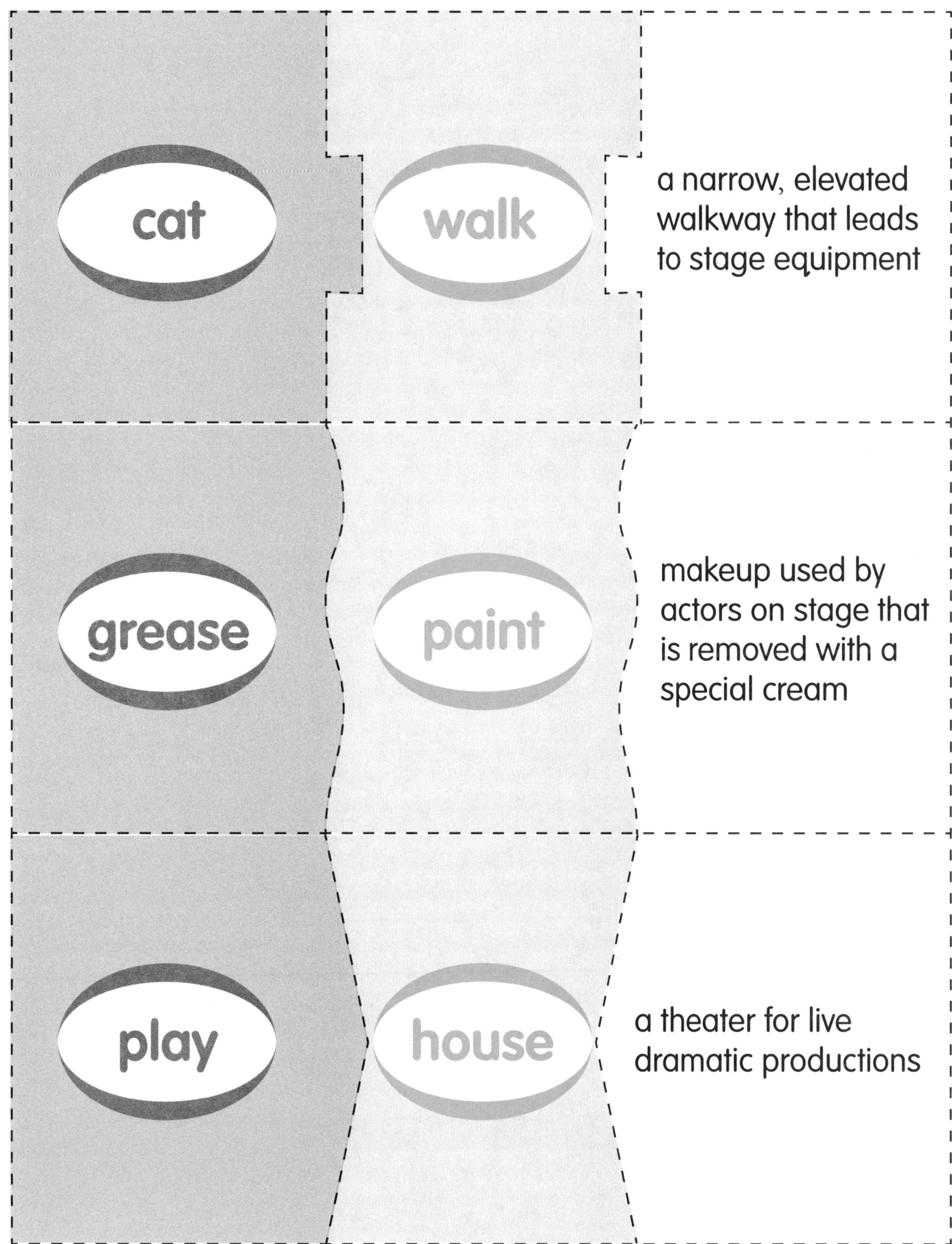
cat
walk
a narrow, elevated walkway that leads to stage equipment
grease
paint
makeup used by actors on stage that is removed with a special cream
play
house
a theater for live dramatic productions

Dramatic Compounds
EMC 3352
© Evan-Moor Corp.

Dramatic Compounds
EMC 3352
© Evan-Moor Corp.

Dramatic Compounds
EMC 3352
© Evan-Moor Corp.

Dramatic Compounds
EMC 3352
© Evan-Moor Corp.

Dramatic Compounds
EMC 3352
© Evan-Moor Corp.

Dramatic Compounds
EMC 3352
© Evan-Moor Corp.

Dramatic Compounds
EMC 3352
© Evan-Moor Corp.

Dramatic Compounds
EMC 3352
© Evan-Moor Corp.

Dramatic Compounds
EMC 3352
© Evan-Moor Corp.

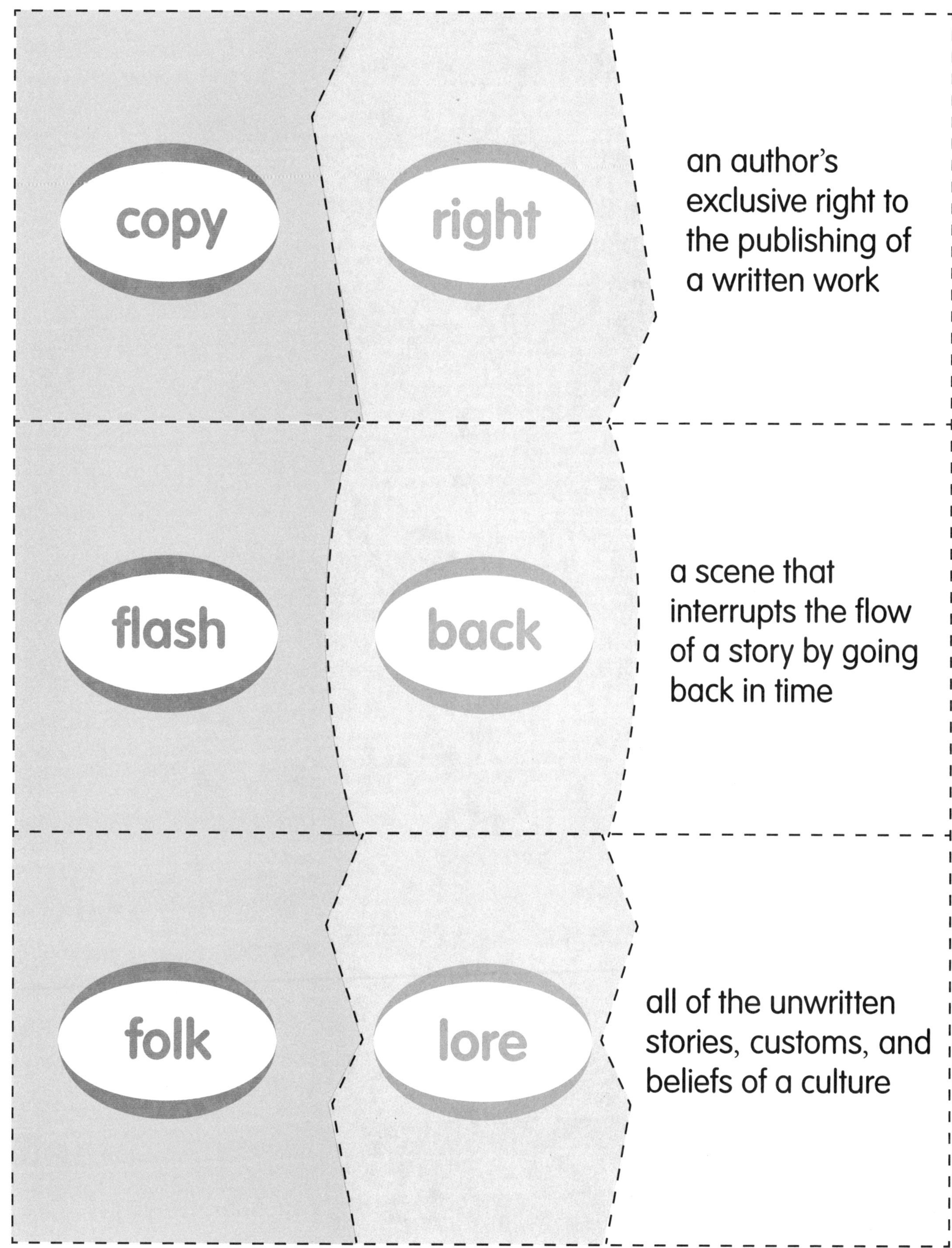
copy
right
an author's exclusive right to the publishing of a written work
flash
back
a scene that interrupts the flow of a story by going back in time
folk
lore
all of the unwritten stories, customs, and beliefs of a culture

Dramatic Compounds

EMC 3352
© Evan-Moor Corp.

Dramatic Compounds

EMC 3352
© Evan-Moor Corp.

Dramatic Compounds

EMC 3352
© Evan-Moor Corp.

Dramatic Compounds

EMC 3352
© Evan-Moor Corp.

Dramatic Compounds

EMC 3352
© Evan-Moor Corp.

Dramatic Compounds

EMC 3352
© Evan-Moor Corp.

Dramatic Compounds

EMC 3352
© Evan-Moor Corp.

Dramatic Compounds

EMC 3352
© Evan-Moor Corp.

Dramatic Compounds

EMC 3352
© Evan-Moor Corp.

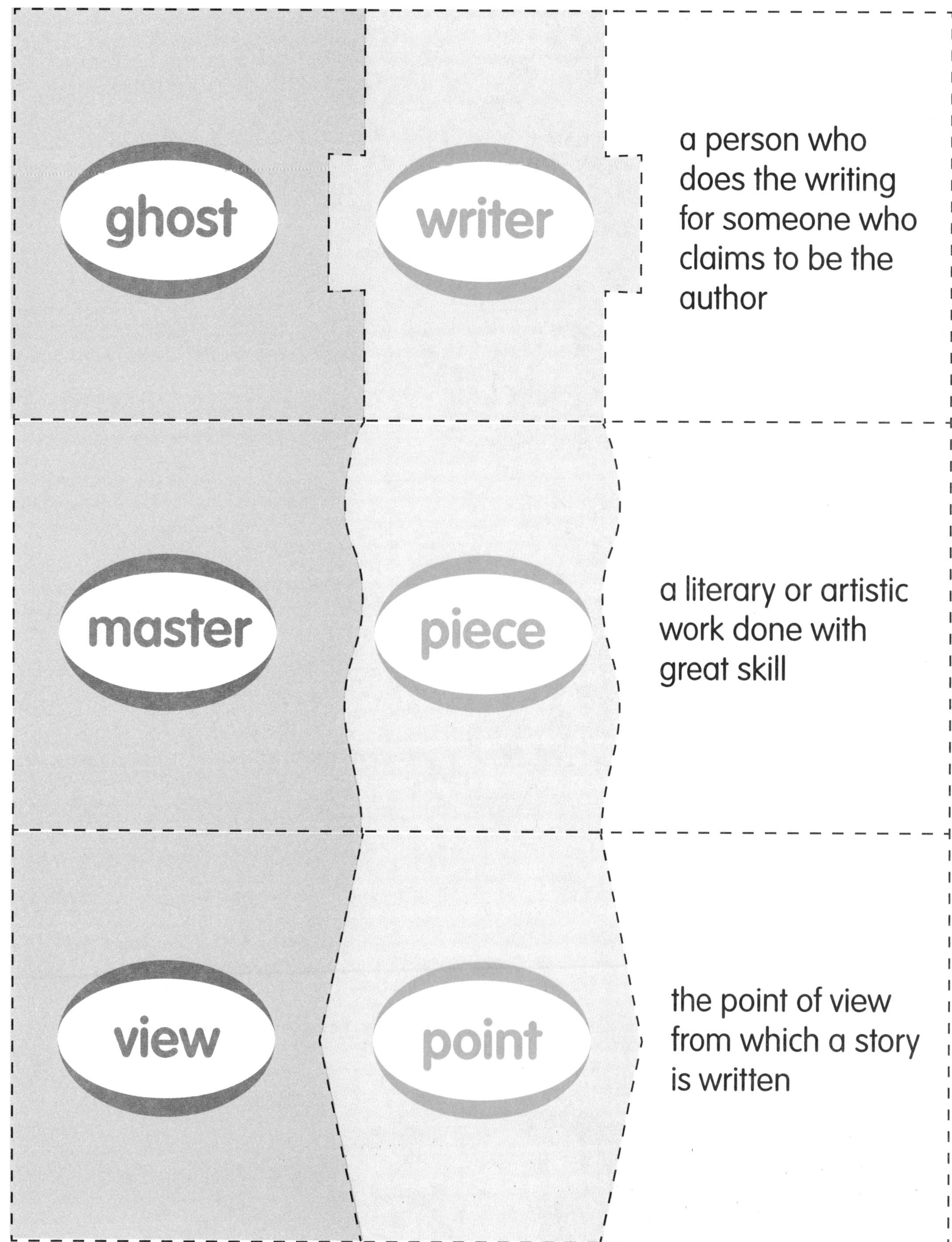
ghost
writer
a person who does the writing for someone who claims to be the author
master
piece
a literary or artistic work done with great skill
view
point
the point of view from which a story is written

Dramatic Compounds

EMC 3352
© Evan-Moor Corp.

Dramatic Compounds

EMC 3352
© Evan-Moor Corp.

Dramatic Compounds

EMC 3352
© Evan-Moor Corp.

Dramatic Compounds

EMC 3352
© Evan-Moor Corp.

Dramatic Compounds

EMC 3352
© Evan-Moor Corp.

Dramatic Compounds

EMC 3352
© Evan-Moor Corp.

Dramatic Compounds

EMC 3352
© Evan-Moor Corp.

Dramatic Compounds

EMC 3352
© Evan-Moor Corp.

Dramatic Compounds

EMC 3352
© Evan-Moor Corp.

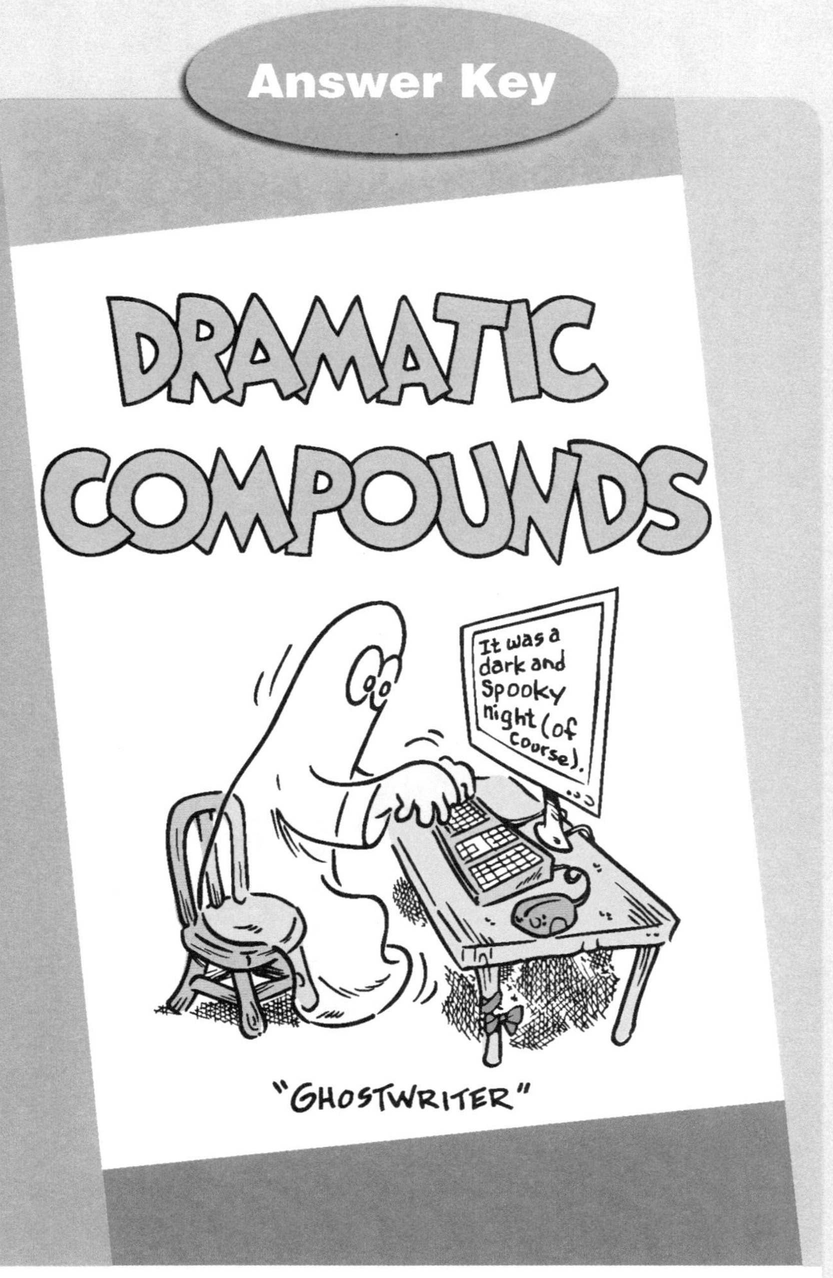

Answer Key
DRAMATIC COMPOUNDS
It was a dark and Spooky night (of course).
"GHOSTWRITER"
Lift the flap to check your answers.

Dramatic Compounds

A Made-up Man

1. playhouse
2. greasepaint
3. catwalk
4. backdrop
5. breakaway
6. blackout

Born to Write

1. ghostwriter
2. masterpiece
3. viewpoint
4. flashback
5. folklore
6. copyright

A Mishmash of Words

Preparing the Center

1. Prepare a folder following the directions on page 3.

   Cover—page 117

   Student Directions—page 119

   Task Cards—pages 121–129

   Answer Key—page 131

2. Reproduce a supply of the activity sheet on page 116. Place copies in the left-hand pocket of the folder.

Partner Practice

1. The students sort the cards into three piles—words, definitions, and sentences.
2. Working together, the students match a word with its definition and the sentence that uses the word correctly. The words are funny-sounding slang words. The cards are self-checking.
3. The students repeat Step 2 to match the other nine sets of cards. Encourage the students to take turns reading the words, definitions, and sentences aloud.
4. Then the students work cooperatively to complete their own activity sheet.
5. Finally, the students check their work using the answer key.

Independent Practice

1. The student sorts the cards into three piles—words, definitions, and sentences.
2. The student matches a word with its definition and the sentence that uses the word correctly. The words are funny-sounding slang words. The cards are self-checking.
3. The student repeats Step 2 to match the other nine sets of cards. Encourage the student to read the words, definitions, and sentences aloud.
4. Then the student completes the activity sheet.
5. Finally, the student self-checks by using the answer key.

Name____ **Activity Sheet**

A Mishmash of Words

Write the slang word on the line that best completes the sentence.
Use the words in the box.

Word Box		
fiddle-faddle	flip-flop	hobnob
hunky-dory	kowtow	lollygag
pell-mell	rinky-dink	topsy-turvy
wheeler-dealer		

1. You shouldn't ________________ since you have a project due Monday.
2. It's ________________ with me if your friends come by to play video games.
3. When the fire alarm rang, the crowd ran ________________ for the exit.
4. Last summer my family stayed in a run-down, ________________ cabin in the woods.
5. Mr. Anderson is a ________________ who buys land cheaply and then sells it for a huge profit.
6. The first-graders sometimes ________________ to the eighth-graders on the playground.
7. Jamie's great-grandmother thinks cell phones are nothing but ________________.
8. Yesterday my parents said I could go to the movies, but today they did a

   ________________ and said no.
9. Peter dreams of becoming rich so he can ________________ with famous people.
10. My kitten knocked the plant ________________ as she dashed by.

A MISHMASH OF WORDS

"RINKY-DINK"

Mishmash of Words

Student Directions

Word Wiz

Slang is made up of colorful, or lively, words and phrases that are used in ordinary conversation. Slang is not used in formal speech or writing.

In this center, old-fashioned, funny-sounding slang words are used.

"My **rinky-dink** car won't even start on a sunny day!" shouted Tim.

Rinky-dink (adjective) means that something is shoddy or worn out, or corny.

Follow These Steps

Partner Practice

1. Sort the cards into three piles—words, definitions, and sentences.
2. Match a slang word with its definition and the sentence that uses the word correctly. Take turns reading the word, definition, and sentence aloud. Turn the cards over to check your work.
3. Repeat Step 2 to match the other nine sets of cards.
4. Work together to complete your own activity sheets.
5. Check your work using the answer key.

Independent Practice

1. Sort the cards into three piles—words, definitions, and sentences.
2. Match a slang word with its definition and the sentence that uses the word correctly, and then read them aloud. Turn the cards over to check your work.
3. Repeat Step 2 to match the other nine sets of cards.
4. Complete the activity sheet.
5. Check your work using the answer key.

fiddle-faddle

(noun)

nonsense

My great-grandfather still uses his typewriter because he thinks computers are ______.

flip-flop

(noun)

a sudden change to an opposite opinion

This morning, Bobby said I could ride his bike, but this afternoon he did a ______.

A Mishmash of Words

EMC 3352 • © Evan-Moor Corp.

A Mishmash of Words

EMC 3352 • © Evan-Moor Corp.

A Mishmash of Words

EMC 3352 • © Evan-Moor Corp.

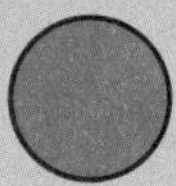

A Mishmash of Words

EMC 3352 • © Evan-Moor Corp.

A Mishmash of Words

EMC 3352 • © Evan-Moor Corp.

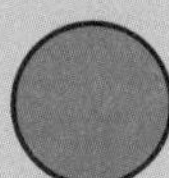

A Mishmash of Words

EMC 3352 • © Evan-Moor Corp.

hobnob
(verb)

to try to be friends with someone important or famous

Tanya wishes she could ______ with the rock star.

hunky-dory
(adjective)

all right; fine

No one can believe that Samson and Lila are ______ together.

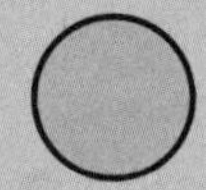

A Mishmash of Words

EMC 3352 • © Evan-Moor Corp.

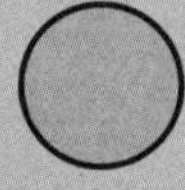

A Mishmash of Words

EMC 3352 • © Evan-Moor Corp.

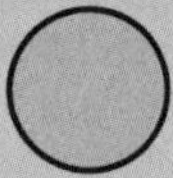

A Mishmash of Words

EMC 3352 • © Evan-Moor Corp.

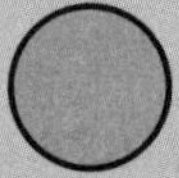

A Mishmash of Words

EMC 3352 • © Evan-Moor Corp.

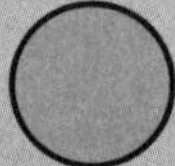

A Mishmash of Words

EMC 3352 • © Evan-Moor Corp.

A Mishmash of Words

EMC 3352 • © Evan-Moor Corp.

kowtow
(verb)

to do things that gain favor or attention

Elena will ______ to her older sister's every wish or demand.

lollygag
(verb)

to fool around or waste time

Zack was supposed to mow the lawn, not ______ on the sofa.

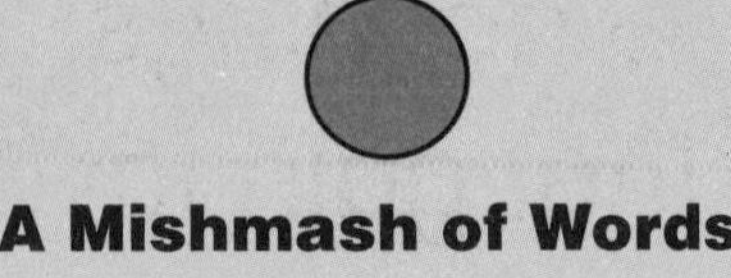

A Mishmash of Words

EMC 3352 • © Evan-Moor Corp.

A Mishmash of Words

EMC 3352 • © Evan-Moor Corp.

A Mishmash of Words

EMC 3352 • © Evan-Moor Corp.

A Mishmash of Words

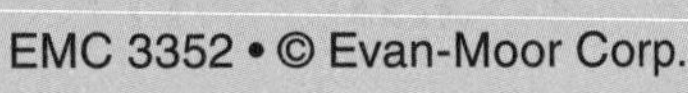

EMC 3352 • © Evan-Moor Corp.

A Mishmash of Words

EMC 3352 • © Evan-Moor Corp.

A Mishmash of Words

EMC 3352 • © Evan-Moor Corp.

pell-mell
(adverb)

in a confused, hurried manner

The fans rushed ______ as the soccer team arrived for the championship match.

topsy-turvy
(adjective)

upside down

Sam tried a new jump and ended up ______ on the ice.

A Mishmash of Words

EMC 3352 • © Evan-Moor Corp.

A Mishmash of Words

EMC 3352 • © Evan-Moor Corp.

A Mishmash of Words

EMC 3352 • © Evan-Moor Corp.

A Mishmash of Words

EMC 3352 • © Evan-Moor Corp.

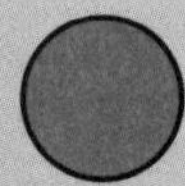

A Mishmash of Words

EMC 3352 • © Evan-Moor Corp.

A Mishmash of Words

EMC 3352 • © Evan-Moor Corp.

rinky-dink
(adjective)

shoddy or
worn out;
corny

Chris was embarrassed by his ______ skateboard.

wheeler-dealer
(noun)

someone who
makes clever
business deals;
a sharp operator

My mother said she would never buy jewelry
from a ______ on a TV commercial.

A Mishmash of Words

EMC 3352 • © Evan-Moor Corp.

A Mishmash of Words

EMC 3352 • © Evan-Moor Corp.

A Mishmash of Words

EMC 3352 • © Evan-Moor Corp.

A Mishmash of Words

EMC 3352 • © Evan-Moor Corp.

A Mishmash of Words

EMC 3352 • © Evan-Moor Corp.

A Mishmash of Words

EMC 3352 • © Evan-Moor Corp.

Answer Key

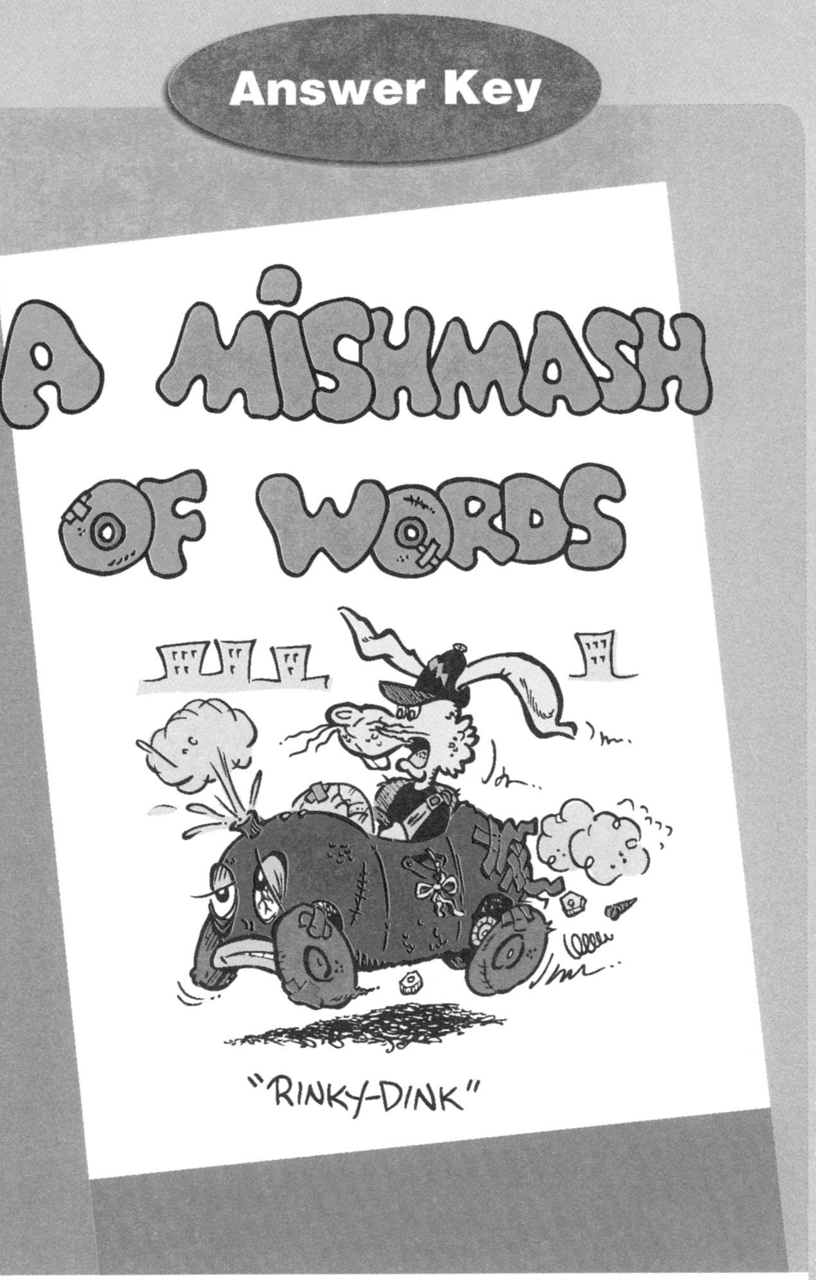

Lift the flap to check your answers.

A Mishmash of Words

1. lollygag
2. hunky-dory
3. pell-mell
4. rinky-dink
5. wheeler-dealer
6. kowtow
7. fiddle-faddle
8. flip-flop
9. hobnob
10. topsy-turvy

Major Biomes

Preparing the Center

1. Prepare a folder following the directions on page 3.

   Cover—page 135

   Student Directions—page 137

   Game Rules—page 139

   Game Board—page 141

   Task Cards—pages 143 and 145

   Answer Key—page 147

2. Reproduce a supply of the activity sheet on page 134. Place copies in the left-hand pocket of the folder.

Partner Practice	Independent Practice
1. The students read the game rules for two players. 2. The students follow the rules to play the game. While they play the game, the students read aloud the name of each biome and its description. 3. Then the students work cooperatively to complete their own activity sheet. 4. Finally, the students check their work using the answer key.	1. The student reads the game rules for one player. 2. The student follows the rules to play the game. While playing the game, the student reads aloud the name of the biome and its description. 3. Then the student completes the activity sheet. 4. Finally, the student self-checks by using the answer key.

Name ____________________

Activity Sheet

Major Biomes

Decide if each statement is true or false. Write your answer on the line.

1. The Arctic tundra consists of permanently frozen subsoil. ____________
2. Temperate grasslands are found in the north-central United States. ____________
3. The savanna biome is found exclusively in Africa. ____________
4. Another name for a boreal forest biome is a taiga. ____________
5. Monkeys and toucans are found in all tropical rainforests. ____________
6. Dense low shrubs grow abundantly in the chaparral biome. ____________
7. Coniferous trees shed their leaves every year. ____________
8. Deserts are found on all seven continents. ____________
9. Mosses, lichens, and sedges are common in the chaparral biome. ____________
10. Maple and elm trees are found in deciduous forests. ____________
11. A tropical rainforest is warm and wet all year long. ____________
12. All coniferous forests are found in the southwestern part of the U.S. ____________

Take It to Your Seat—Vocabulary Centers • EMC 3352 • © Evan-Moor Corp.

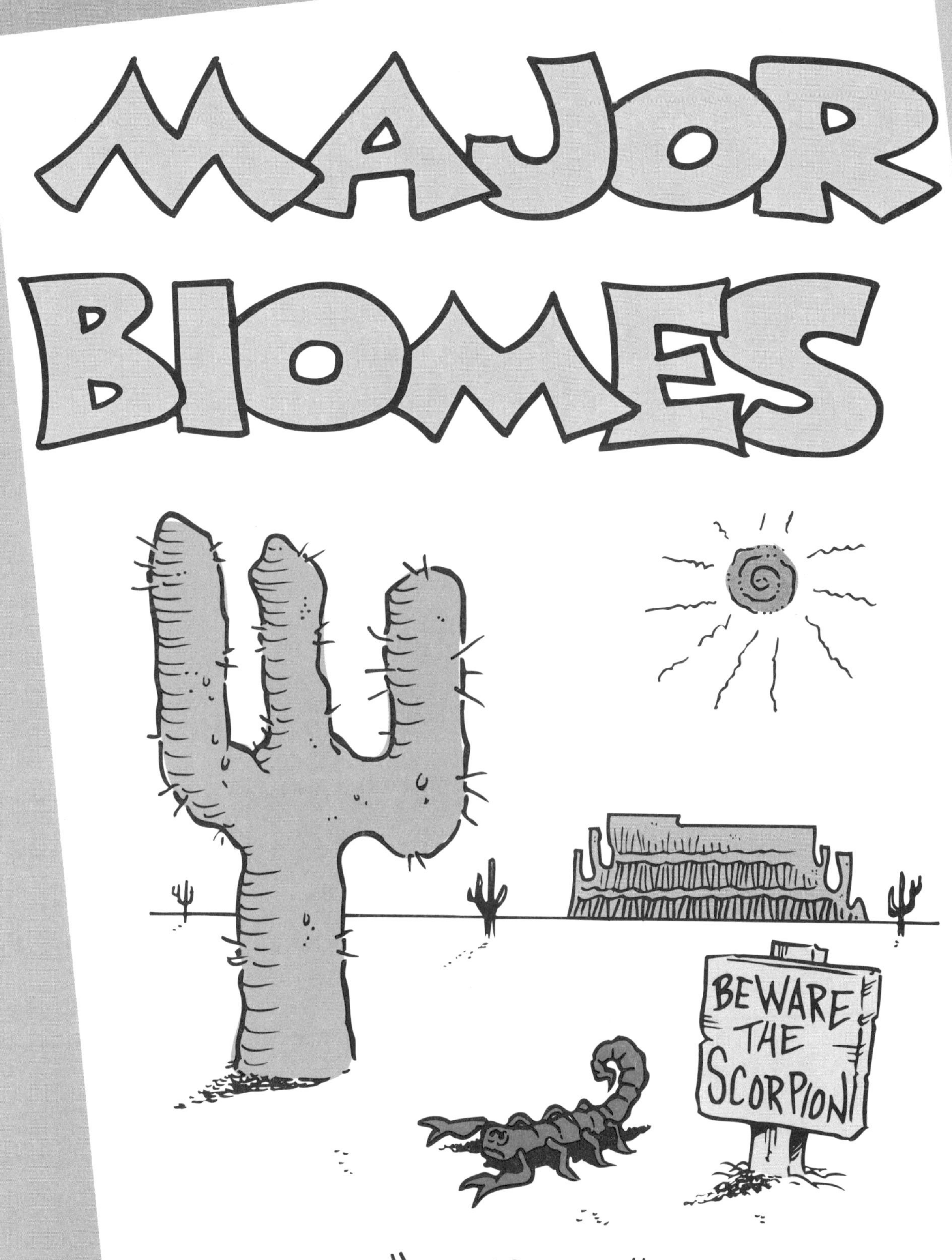
MAJOR
BIOMES
BEWARE
THE
SCORPION
"DESERT"

Major Biomes

Student Directions

Word Wiz

Science words are important to know.
Biome (**by**-ohm) is a science word. A biome is a community of plants and animals that covers a large geographical area.

There are land biomes and water biomes.

Major Land Biomes				
boreal forest (taiga)	coniferous forest	desert	rainforest	tundra
chaparral	deciduous forest	grassland	savanna	

Follow These Steps

Partner Practice

1. Read the tic-tac-toe rules for two players.
2. Play the game. Read aloud each biome name and its description as you play.
3. Work together to complete your own activity sheet.
4. Check your work using the answer key.

Independent Practice

1. Read the tic-tac-toe rules for one player.
2. Play the game. Read aloud each biome name and its description as you play.
3. Complete the activity sheet.
4. Check your work using the answer key.

Rules for 2 Players:

1. Choose which player will have the X word cards and which player will have the O word cards.
2. Take your cards and keep them in a pile, description side up. Set the tic-tac-toe game board between the two of you.
3. Let player X go first. The player reads aloud the first X card and its description. Then the player turns over the card and places it on the matching space on the game board.
4. Player O goes next. The player reads aloud the first O card and its description. Then the player turns over the card and places it on the matching space on the game board.
5. Take turns playing until one player has three words in a row. Or, play until the game board is covered, and no one has won.

Rules for 1 Player:

1. Shuffle the X cards and place them in a pile, description side up. Do the same for the O cards.
2. Pick the top card from the X pile. Read aloud the card and its description.
3. Place the X card on the matching space on the game board.
4. Then repeat Steps 2 and 3 with the top card from the O pile.
5. Continue playing until you have three X words or three O words in a row, or until you cover the game board.

Take It to Your Seat—Vocabulary Centers • EMC 3352 • © Evan-Moor Corp.

MAJOR BIOMES

Boreal Forest or Taiga	Chaparral	Desert
Grassland	Savanna	Coniferous Forest
Deciduous Forest	Rainforest	Tundra

Boreal Forest
Chaparral
Desert
Grassland
Savanna
Coniferous Forest
Deciduous Forest
Rainforest
Tundra

Desert

- Extremely dry; most are hot; some are cold
- Found on every continent
- American desert plants: variety of cacti
- U.S. animals: lizards, scorpions, and kangaroo rats

Major Biomes
EMC 3352 • © Evan-Moor Corp.

Chaparral

- Hot, dry summers and cool, rainy winters
- Found along western coasts of North and South America, areas around Mediterranean Sea, South Africa, and Australia
- Plants: dense low shrubs
- U.S. animals: mountain lions, quail, and mule deer

Major Biomes
EMC 3352 • © Evan-Moor Corp.

Boreal Forest or Taiga (**ty**-guh)

- Cold winters, short growing season
- Found in Alaska, Canada, and northern parts of Europe and Asia
- Plants: cone-producing evergreen trees such as fir and spruce
- Animals: bears, moose, and wolves

Major Biomes
EMC 3352 • © Evan-Moor Corp.

Coniferous Forest

(kuh-**nif**-ur-uhss)

- Mild temperatures and heavy rain
- Found mostly on Pacific Coast of North America
- Plants: cone-bearing evergreens such as cedar and pine
- Animals: black bears, beavers, and owls

Major Biomes
EMC 3352 • © Evan-Moor Corp.

Savanna

- Tropical grassland with long dry season
- Found in Africa, Australia, and South America
- Plants: tall grasses and drought-resistant trees and shrubs
- African animals: lions, giraffes, and zebras

Major Biomes
EMC 3352 • © Evan-Moor Corp.

Grassland

- Moderate, humid climate
- Found in north-central U.S., central Asia, and central Europe
- Plants: tall prairie grasses and herbs
- U.S. animals: prairie dogs, badgers, and antelope

Major Biomes
EMC 3352 • © Evan-Moor Corp.

Deciduous Forest

(di-**sij**-oo-uhss)

- Warm summers and cold winters
- Found in eastern U.S., Europe, and eastern Asia
- U.S. plants: trees that shed their leaves every year such as maples, oaks, and elms
- U.S. animals: deer, squirrels, and skunks

Major Biomes
EMC 3352 • © Evan-Moor Corp.

Rainforest

- Tropical; warm and wet all year
- Found in Central and South America and parts of Africa, Asia, and Australia
- Plants: tall evergreen trees, ferns, and vines
- South American animals: monkeys, jaguars, and toucans

Major Biomes
EMC 3352 • © Evan-Moor Corp.

Tundra

- Extremely cold, dry; permanently frozen subsoil
- Found in the Arctic regions of Alaska, Canada, Europe, and Russia
- Plants: mosses, lichens, and sedges (grasslike plants)
- Animals: arctic fox, polar bears, and snowy owls

Major Biomes
EMC 3352 • © Evan-Moor Corp.

Boreal Forest
Chaparral
Desert
Grassland
Savanna
Coniferous Forest
Deciduous Forest
Rainforest
Tundra

Desert

- Extremely dry; most are hot; some are cold
- Found on every continent
- American desert plants: variety of cacti
- U.S. animals: lizards, scorpions, and kangaroo rats

Major Biomes
EMC 3352 • © Evan-Moor Corp.

Chaparral

- Hot, dry summers and cool, rainy winters
- Found along western coasts of North and South America, areas around Mediterranean Sea, South Africa, and Australia
- Plants: dense low shrubs
- U.S. animals: mountain lions, quail, and mule deer

Major Biomes
EMC 3352 • © Evan-Moor Corp.

Boreal Forest or Taiga (**ty**-guh)

- Cold winters, short growing season
- Found in Alaska, Canada, and northern parts of Europe and Asia
- Plants: cone-producing evergreen trees such as fir and spruce
- Animals: bears, moose, and wolves

Major Biomes
EMC 3352 • © Evan-Moor Corp.

Coniferous Forest (kuh-**nif**-ur-uhss)

- Mild temperatures and heavy rain
- Found mostly on Pacific Coast of North America
- Plants: cone-bearing evergreens such as cedar and pine
- Animals: black bears, beavers, and owls

Major Biomes
EMC 3352 • © Evan-Moor Corp.

Savanna

- Tropical grassland with long dry season
- Found in Africa, Australia, and South America
- Plants: tall grasses and drought-resistant trees and shrubs
- African animals: lions, giraffes, and zebras

Major Biomes
EMC 3352 • © Evan-Moor Corp.

Grassland

- Moderate, humid climate
- Found in north-central U.S., central Asia, and central Europe
- Plants: tall prairie grasses and herbs
- U.S. animals: prairie dogs, badgers, and antelope

Major Biomes
EMC 3352 • © Evan-Moor Corp.

Deciduous Forest (di-**sij**-oo-uhss)

- Warm summers and cold winters
- Found in eastern U.S., Europe, and eastern Asia
- U.S. plants: trees that shed their leaves every year such as maples, oaks, and elms
- U.S. animals: deer, squirrels, and skunks

Major Biomes
EMC 3352 • © Evan-Moor Corp.

Rainforest

- Tropical; warm and wet all year
- Found in Central and South America and parts of Africa, Asia, and Australia
- Plants: tall evergreen trees, ferns, and vines
- South American animals: monkeys, jaguars, and toucans

Major Biomes
EMC 3352 • © Evan-Moor Corp.

Tundra

- Extremely cold, dry; permanently frozen subsoil
- Found in the Arctic regions of Alaska, Canada, Europe, and Russia
- Plants: mosses, lichens, and sedges (grasslike plants)
- Animals: arctic fox, polar bears, and snowy owls

Major Biomes
EMC 3352 • © Evan-Moor Corp.

Answer Key

MAJOR BIOMES

BEWARE THE SCORPION!

"DESERT"

Lift the flap to check your answers.

Major Biomes

1. true
2. true
3. false
4. true
5. false
6. true
7. false
8. true
9. false
10. true
11. true
12. false

Geometry Terms

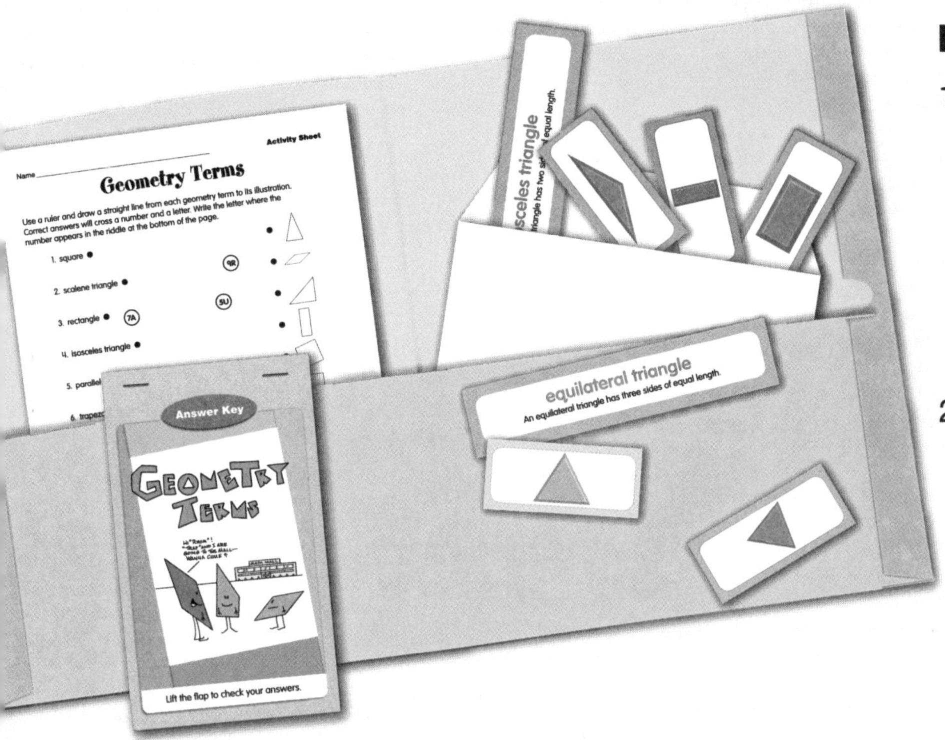

Preparing the Center

1. Prepare a folder following the directions on page 3.

   Cover—page 151

   Student Directions—page 153

   Task Cards—pages 155–159

   Answer Key—page 161

2. Reproduce a supply of the activity sheet on page 150. Place copies in the left-hand pocket of the folder.

Partner Practice

1. Students sort the cards into two piles—defined geometry terms and geometric figures.
2. Working together, the students match a geometry term with its two corresponding figures. The cards are self-checking.
3. The students repeat Step 2 to complete the other eight matches. Encourage the students to take turns reading the terms and definitions aloud.
4. Then the students work cooperatively to complete their own activity sheet.
5. Finally, the students check their work using the answer key.

Independent Practice

1. The student sorts the cards into two piles—defined geometry terms and geometric figures.
2. The student matches a geometry term with its two corresponding figures. The cards are self-checking.
3. The student repeats Step 2 to complete the other eight matches. Encourage the student to read the terms and definitions aloud.
4. Then the student completes the activity sheet.
5. Finally, the student self-checks by using the answer key.

Name ______________________________ **Activity Sheet**

Geometry Terms

Use a ruler and draw a straight line from each geometry term to its illustration. Correct answers will cross a number and a letter. Write the letter where the number appears in the riddle at the bottom of the page.

1. square ● 

2. scalene triangle ●  ●

3. rectangle ●  5U ● 

4. isosceles triangle ● ● 

5. parallelogram ● ● 

6. trapezoid ● 2P  8E 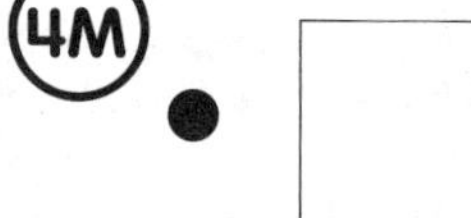

7. equilateral triangle ● 6U ●

8. right triangle ● 1E ●

9. rhombus ● ●

What did the proud ruler say to the protractor?

We both ___ ___ ___ ___ ___ ___ ___   ___ ___!
4 8 7 3 5 9 1   6 2

Take It to Your Seat—Vocabulary Centers • EMC 3352 • © Evan-Moor Corp.

Geometry Terms

Geometry Terms

Student Directions

Word Wiz

Triangles are three-sided figures. **Quadrilaterals** are four-sided figures. Triangles and quadrilaterals can have different shapes.

In this center, you will work with four different triangles and five different quadrilaterals.

The three sides of an **equilateral triangle** are all of equal length.

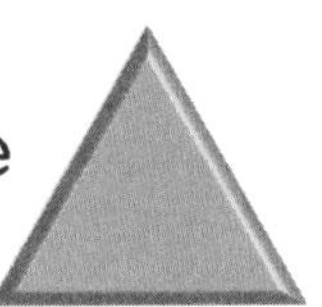

The four sides of a **square** are all of equal length.

Follow These Steps

Partner Practice

1. Sort the cards into two piles—geometry terms and geometric figures.
2. Match a geometry term with its two corresponding figures. Take turns reading aloud the term and its definition. Turn the set of three cards over to check your work.
3. Repeat Step 2 to match all the other sets of cards.
4. Work together to complete your own activity sheet.
5. Check your work using the answer key.

Independent Practice

1. Sort the cards into two piles—geometry terms and geometric figures.
2. Match a geometry term with its two corresponding figures. Read the term and its definition aloud. Turn the set of three cards over to check your work.
3. Repeat Step 2 to match all the other sets of cards.
4. Complete the activity sheet.
5. Check your work using the answer key.

equilateral triangle

An equilateral triangle has three sides of equal length.

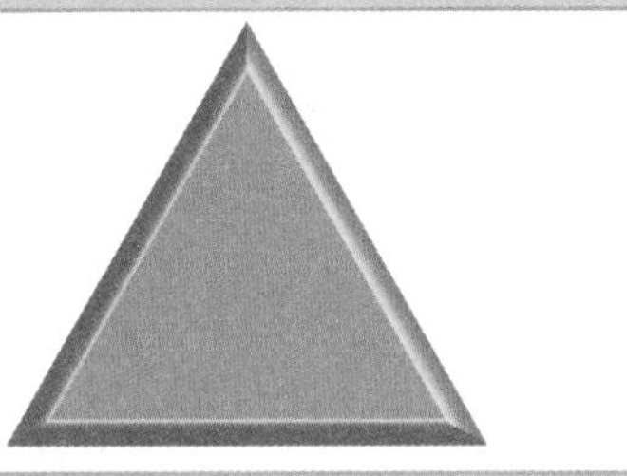

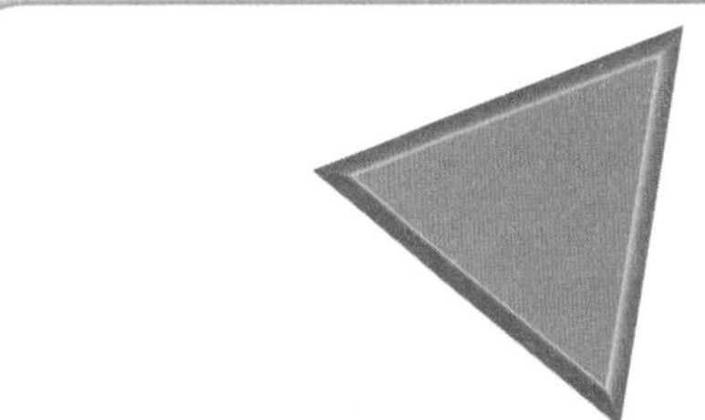

isosceles triangle

An isosceles triangle has two sides of equal length.

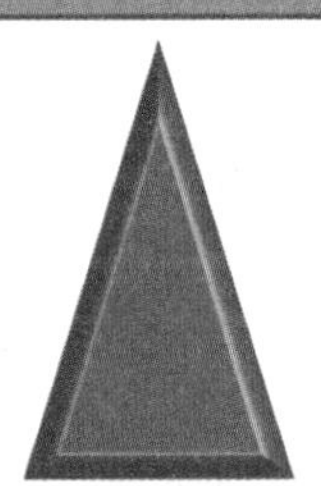

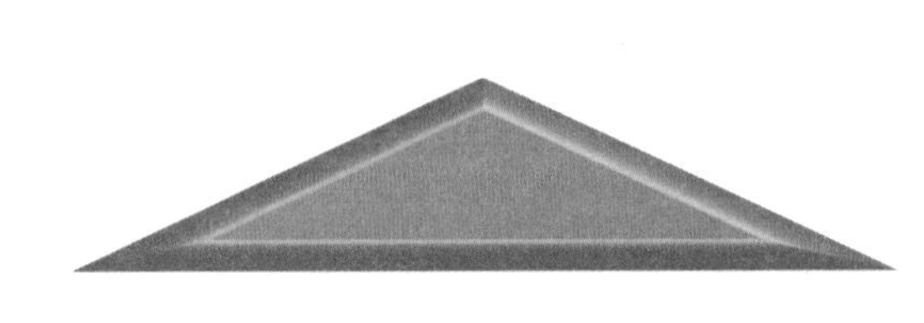

right triangle

A right triangle has two line segments that form a right angle.

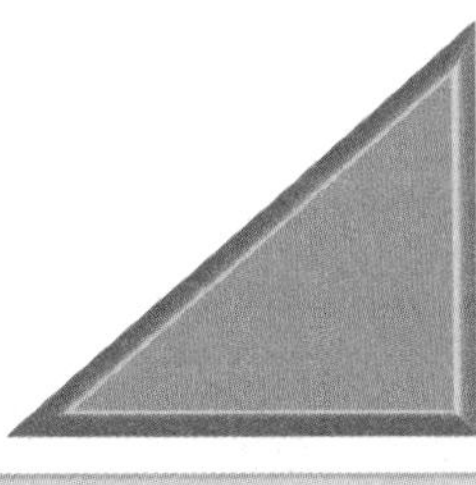

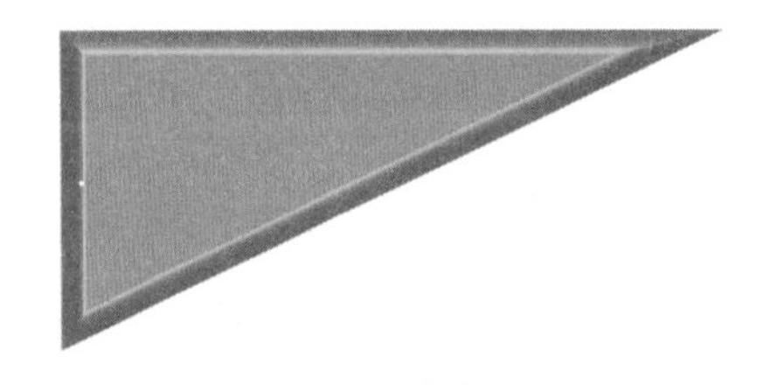

Geometry Terms

EMC 3352 • © Evan-Moor Corp.

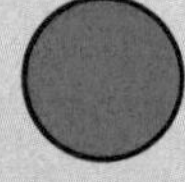

Geometry Terms

EMC 3352 • © Evan-Moor Corp.

Geometry Terms

EMC 3352 • © Evan-Moor Corp.

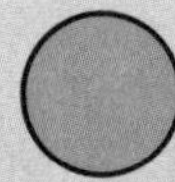

Geometry Terms

EMC 3352 • © Evan-Moor Corp.

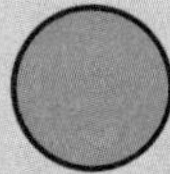

Geometry Terms

EMC 3352 • © Evan-Moor Corp.

Geometry Terms

EMC 3352 • © Evan-Moor Corp.

Geometry Terms

EMC 3352 • © Evan-Moor Corp.

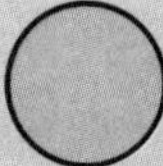

Geometry Terms

EMC 3352 • © Evan-Moor Corp.

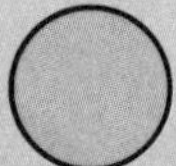

Geometry Terms

EMC 3352 • © Evan-Moor Corp.

scalene triangle

A scalene triangle has three sides of different lengths.

parallelogram

A parallelogram is a four-sided figure that has two pairs of parallel sides.

rectangle

A rectangle is a four-sided figure that has four right angles.

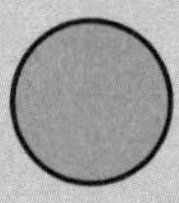

Geometry Terms

EMC 3352 • © Evan-Moor Corp.

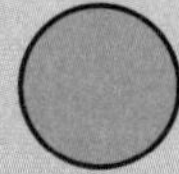

Geometry Terms

EMC 3352 • © Evan-Moor Corp.

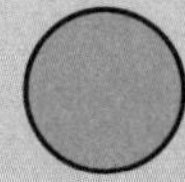

Geometry Terms

EMC 3352 • © Evan-Moor Corp.

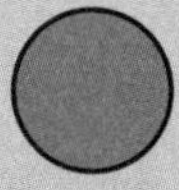

Geometry Terms

EMC 3352 • © Evan-Moor Corp.

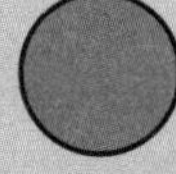

Geometry Terms

EMC 3352 • © Evan-Moor Corp.

Geometry Terms

EMC 3352 • © Evan-Moor Corp.

Geometry Terms

EMC 3352 • © Evan-Moor Corp.

Geometry Terms

EMC 3352 • © Evan-Moor Corp.

Geometry Terms

EMC 3352 • © Evan-Moor Corp.

rhombus

A rhombus is a parallelogram whose sides are of equal length.

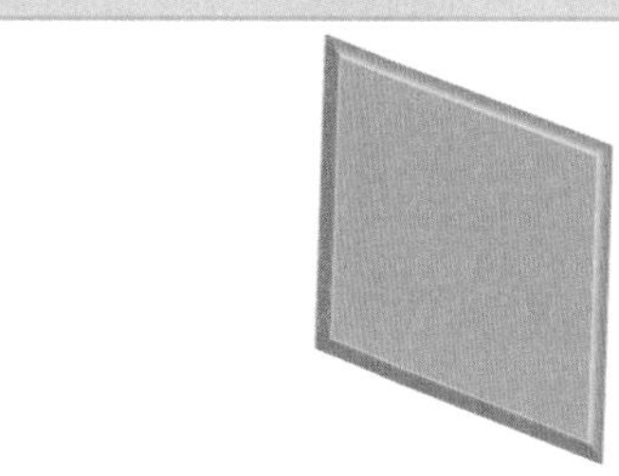

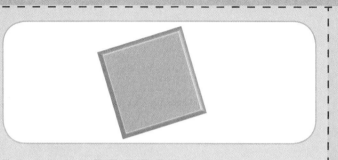

square

A square is a rectangle whose sides are of equal length.

trapezoid

A trapezoid is a four-sided figure with one pair of parallel sides.

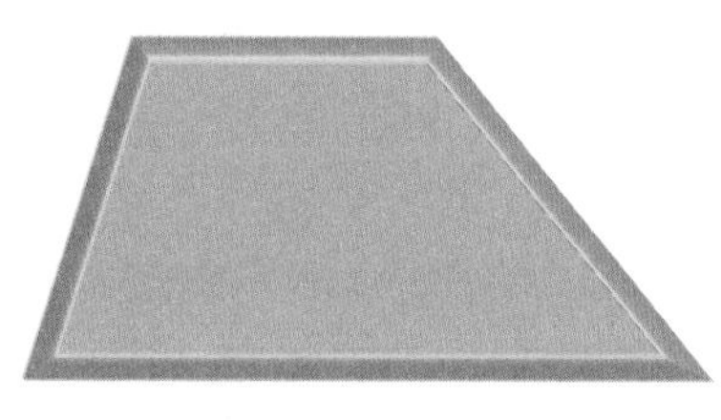

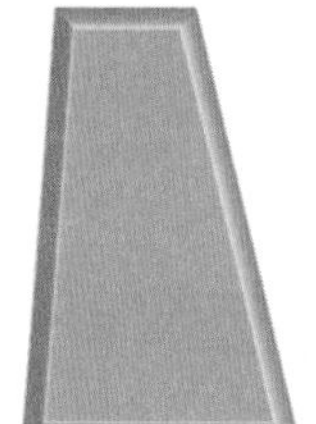

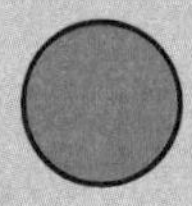

Geometry Terms

EMC 3352 • © Evan-Moor Corp.

Geometry Terms

EMC 3352 • © Evan-Moor Corp.

Geometry Terms

EMC 3352 • © Evan-Moor Corp.

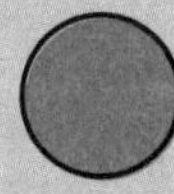

Geometry Terms

EMC 3352 • © Evan-Moor Corp.

Geometry Terms

EMC 3352 • © Evan-Moor Corp.

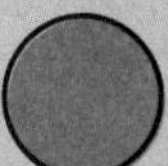

Geometry Terms

EMC 3352 • © Evan-Moor Corp.

Geometry Terms

EMC 3352 • © Evan-Moor Corp.

Geometry Terms

EMC 3352 • © Evan-Moor Corp.

Geometry Terms

EMC 3352 • © Evan-Moor Corp.

Answer Key

GEOMETRY TERMS

HI "RHOM"! "TRAP" AND I ARE GOING TO THE MALL— WANNA COME?

MATH MALL

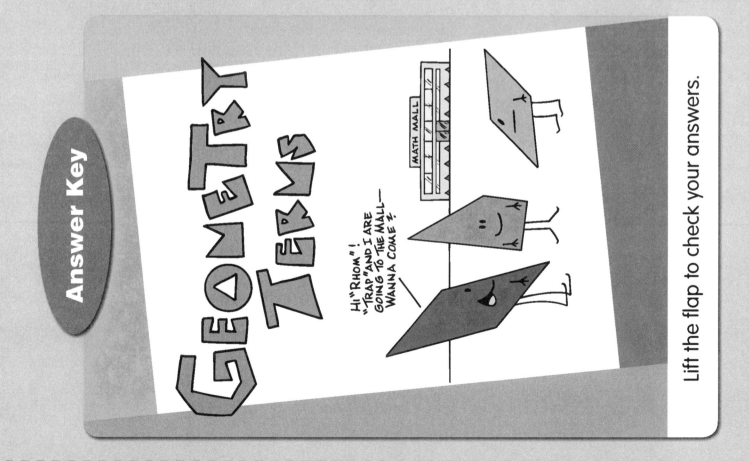

Lift the flap to check your answers.

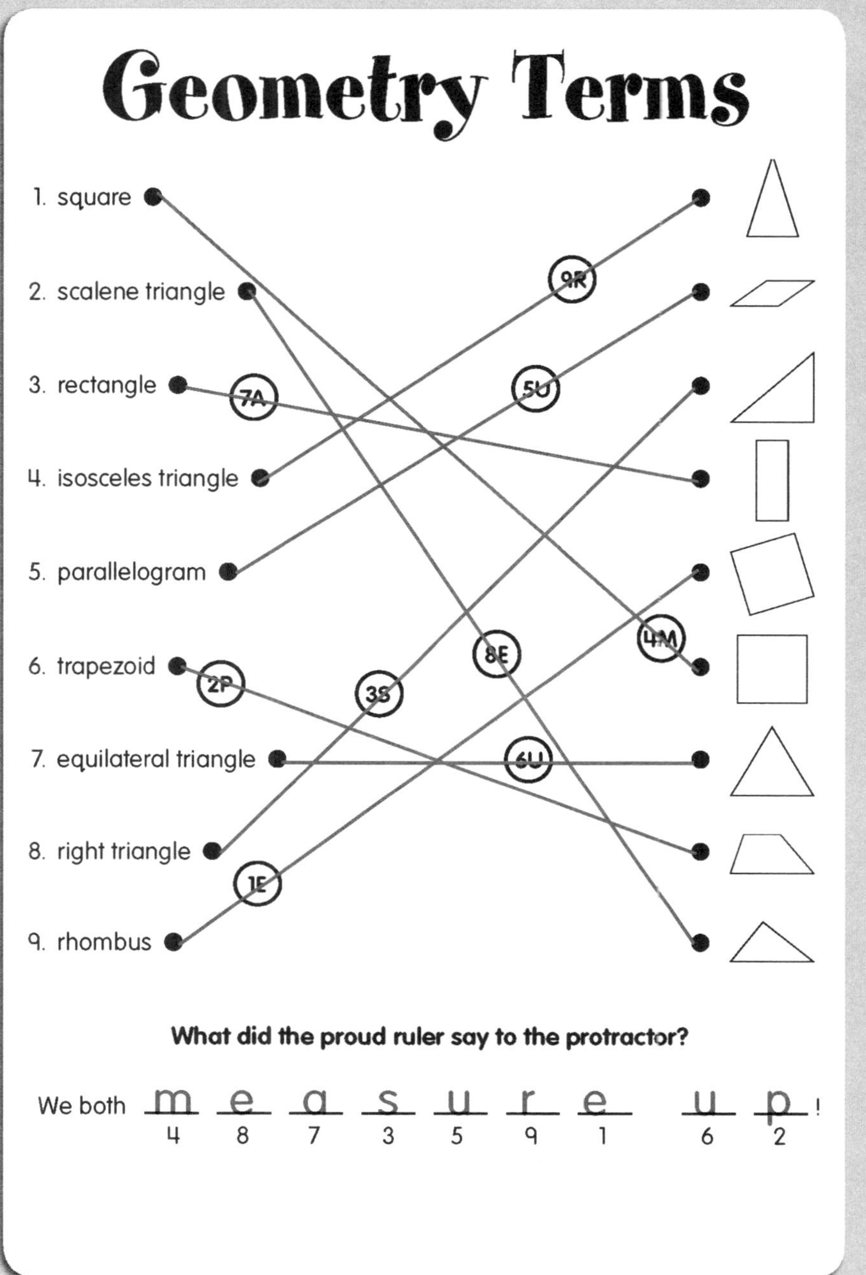

French Sayings

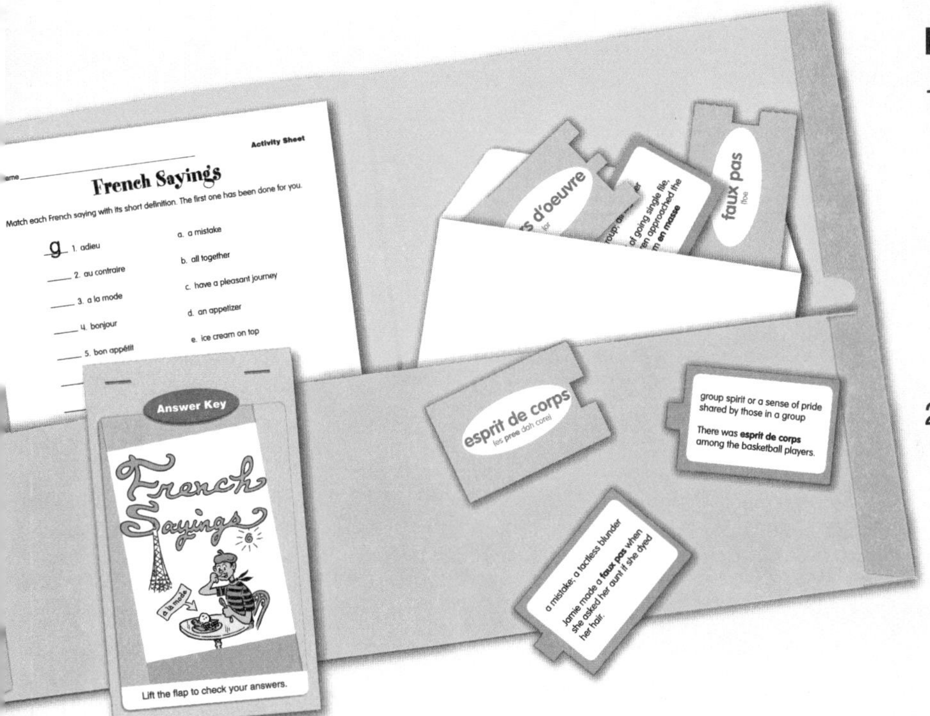

Preparing the Center

1. Prepare a folder following the directions on page 3.

   Cover—page 165

   Student Directions—page 167

   Puzzle Pieces—pages 169–173

   Answer Key—page 175

2. Reproduce a supply of the activity sheet on page 164. Place copies in the left-hand pocket of the folder.

Partner Practice	Independent Practice
1. The students sort the puzzle pieces into two piles—French sayings and definitions/sentences. 2. Working together, the students form a two-part puzzle by matching a French saying to its definition/sentence. 3. The students repeat Step 2 to complete the other 11 puzzles. Encourage the students to take turns pronouncing the French sayings aloud. 4. Then the students work cooperatively to complete their own activity sheet. 5. Finally, the students check their work using the answer key.	1. The student sorts the puzzle pieces into two piles—French sayings and definitions/sentences. 2. The student matches a French saying to its definition/sentence to form a two-part puzzle. 3. The student repeats Step 2 to complete the other 11 puzzles. Encourage the student to pronounce the French sayings aloud. 4. Then the student completes the activity sheet. 5. Finally, the student self-checks by using the answer key.

Name ________________________________ **Activity Sheet**

French Sayings

Match each French saying with its short definition. The first one has been done for you.

__g__ 1. adieu	a. a mistake
____ 2. au contraire	b. all together
____ 3. à la mode	c. have a pleasant journey
____ 4. bonjour	d. an appetizer
____ 5. bon appétit	e. ice cream on top
____ 6. bon voyage	f. hello
____ 7. esprit de corps	g. good-bye
____ 8. faux pas	h. individual items on a menu
____ 9. cul-de-sac	i. enjoy your meal
____ 10. en masse	j. a dead-end street
____ 11. à la carte	k. opposite
____ 12. hors d'oeuvre	l. group spirit

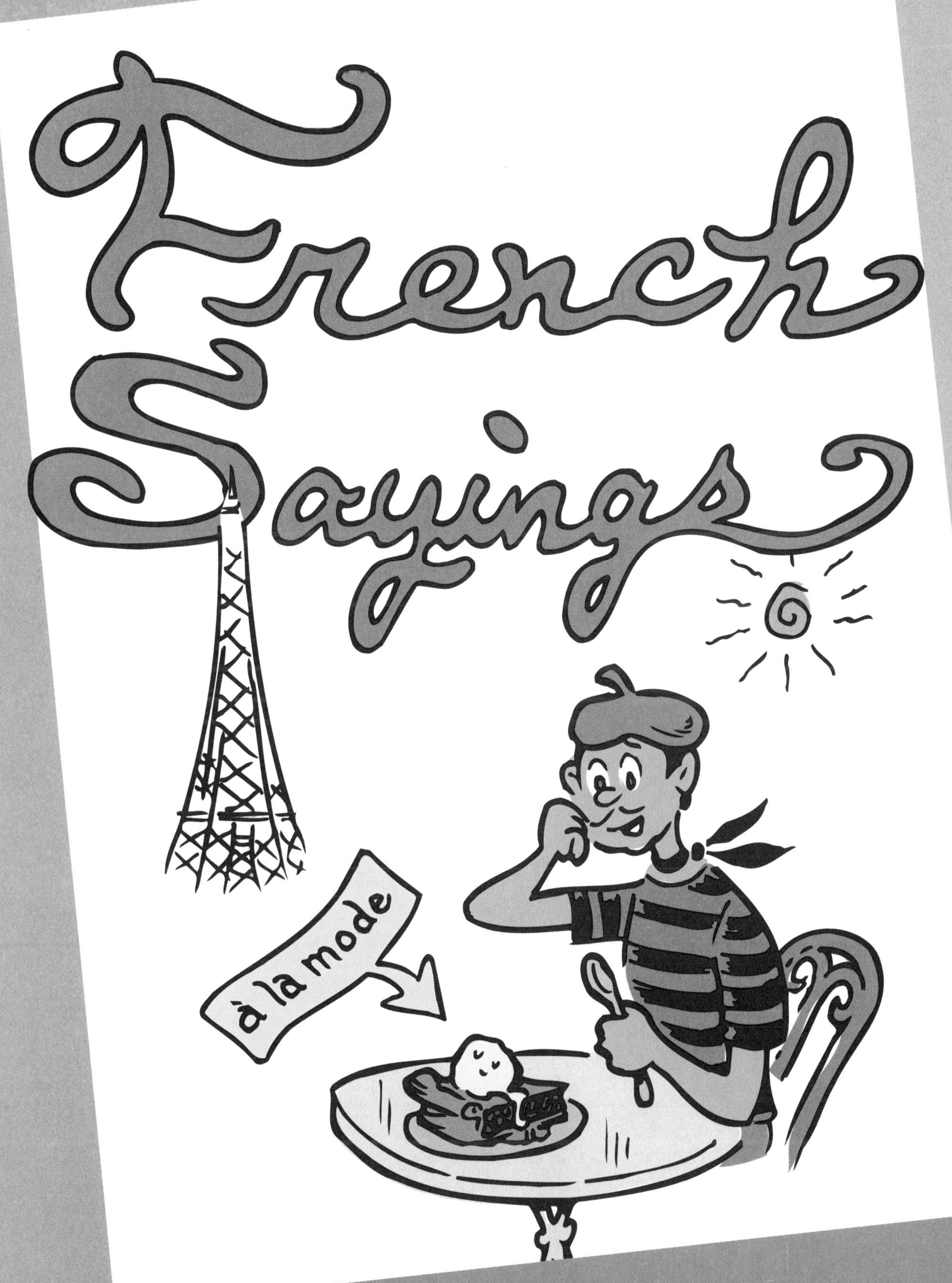
French Sayings
à la mode

French Sayings

Student Directions

Word Wiz

French words and phrases are commonly used by English speakers and writers. The words and phrases are fun to pronounce.

The French phrase **à la mode** is commonly used in the United States.

In French, the phrase means "in fashion or stylish."

In America, the phrase indicates desserts served with ice cream.

You might like your apple pie **à la mode**.

Follow These Steps

Partner Practice

1. Sort the puzzle pieces into two piles—French sayings and definitions/sentences.
2. Working together, match a French saying to its definition/sentence to complete a puzzle.
3. Repeat Step 2 to complete the other 11 puzzles. Take turns reading the French sayings aloud. Use the pronunciations of the sayings to help you.
4. Work together to complete your own activity sheet.
5. Check your work using the answer key.

Independent Practice

1. Sort the puzzle pieces into two piles—French sayings and definitions/sentences.
2. Match a French saying to its definition/sentence to complete a puzzle.
3. Repeat Step 2 to complete the other 11 puzzles. Use the pronunciations of the sayings to help you read them aloud.
4. Complete the activity sheet.
5. Check your work using the answer key.

à la carte
(ah lah **cart**)

said when ordering individual items from the menu instead of a complete dinner

I would like to order **à la carte** instead of getting the three-course dinner.

à la mode
(ah lah **mode**)

said when you want ice cream on top of your dessert

Please make my cherry pie **à la mode.**

au contraire
(oh con-**trair**)

on the contrary, or opposite

Her opinion on the need for year-round school was **au contraire** from mine.

bon appétit
(bone ah-pay-**tee**)

said before eating; enjoy your meal

Before we began eating our Thanksgiving dinner, Grandpa said **bon appétit** to everyone.

French Sayings

EMC 3352 • © Evan-Moor Corp.

French Sayings

EMC 3352 • © Evan-Moor Corp.

French Sayings

EMC 3352 • © Evan-Moor Corp.

French Sayings

EMC 3352 • © Evan-Moor Corp.

French Sayings

EMC 3352 • © Evan-Moor Corp.

French Sayings

EMC 3352 • © Evan-Moor Corp.

French Sayings

EMC 3352 • © Evan-Moor Corp.

French Sayings

EMC 3352 • © Evan-Moor Corp.

bonjour
(bōn-**zhoor**)

a greeting; good day or hello

The friendly neighbor said **bonjour** to the children on their way to school.

bon voyage
(bon voi-**ahj**)

a farewell to a traveler; have a pleasant journey

We said **bon voyage** to Uncle Max as he departed for Australia.

adieu
(ah-**dyoo**)

a good-bye or farewell greeting

I bid my cousin a fond **adieu** at the end of the party.

cul-de-sac
(**kuhl**-dah-sak)

a dead-end street with a turnaround at the closed end

Shelby lives on a quiet **cul-de-sac.**

French Sayings

EMC 3352 • © Evan-Moor Corp.

French Sayings

EMC 3352 • © Evan-Moor Corp.

French Sayings

EMC 3352 • © Evan-Moor Corp.

French Sayings

EMC 3352 • © Evan-Moor Corp.

French Sayings

EMC 3352 • © Evan-Moor Corp.

French Sayings

EMC 3352 • © Evan-Moor Corp.

French Sayings

EMC 3352 • © Evan-Moor Corp.

French Sayings

EMC 3352 • © Evan-Moor Corp.

esprit de corps
(es-**pree** dah core)

group spirit or a sense of pride shared by those in a group

There was **esprit de corps** among the basketball players.

faux pas
(foe **paw**)

a mistake; a tactless blunder

Jamie made a **faux pas** when she asked her aunt if she dyed her hair.

en masse
(en **mass**)

in a group; all together

Instead of going single file, the children approached the gymnasium **en masse**.

hors d'oeuvre
(or **durv**)

a small portion of food served as an appetizer before a meal

Aunt Kate can't eat just one shrimp **hors d'oeuvre.**

French Sayings

EMC 3352 • © Evan-Moor Corp.

French Sayings

EMC 3352 • © Evan-Moor Corp.

French Sayings

EMC 3352 • © Evan-Moor Corp.

French Sayings

EMC 3352 • © Evan-Moor Corp.

French Sayings

EMC 3352 • © Evan-Moor Corp.

French Sayings

EMC 3352 • © Evan-Moor Corp.

French Sayings

EMC 3352 • © Evan-Moor Corp.

French Sayings

EMC 3352 • © Evan-Moor Corp.

Lift the flap to check your answers.

French Sayings

1. g
2. k
3. e
4. f
5. i
6. c
7. l
8. a
9. j
10. b
11. h
12. d

Choosing Homographs

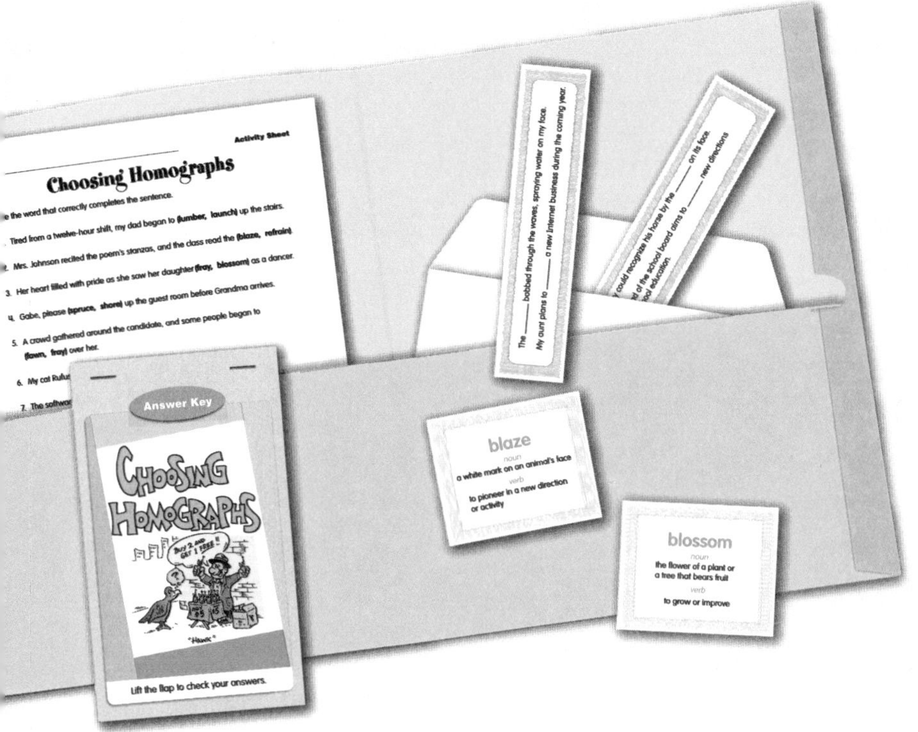

Preparing the Center

1. Prepare a folder following the directions on page 3.

   Cover—page 179

   Student Directions—page 181

   Task Cards—pages 183–189

   Answer Key—page 191

2. Reproduce a supply of the activity sheet on page 178. Place copies in the left-hand pocket of the folder.

Partner Practice	Independent Practice
1. The students sort the cards into two piles—sentences and homographs. 2. Working together, the students read each pair of sentences aloud. They find the word that correctly completes both sentences. The students turn over each set of cards to check their work. 3. Then the students work cooperatively to complete their own activity sheet. 4. Finally, the students check their work using the answer key.	1. The student sorts the cards into two piles—sentences and homographs. 2. The student reads aloud each pair of sentences. The student finds the word that correctly completes both sentences. The student turns over each set of cards to self-check. 3. Then the student completes the activity sheet. 4. Finally, the student self-checks by using the answer key.

Name ____________________ **Activity Sheet**

Choosing Homographs

Circle the word that correctly completes each sentence.

1. Tired from a twelve-hour shift, my dad began to **(lumber, launch)** up the stairs.
2. Mrs. Johnson recited the poem's stanzas, and the class read the **(blaze, refrain)**.
3. Her heart filled with pride as she saw her daughter **(fray, blossom)** as a dancer.
4. Gabe, please **(spruce, shore)** up the guest room before Grandma arrives.
5. A crowd gathered around the candidate, and some people began to **(fawn, fray)** over her.
6. My cat Rufus is all black except for a **(blossom, blaze)** on his face.
7. The software company will **(launch, spruce)** a new television commercial during the holidays.
8. The **(spruce, hawk)** used its talons to clasp the field mouse.
9. The team mascot wears the school colors, which are gold and **(maroon, refrain)**.
10. A sand castle-building contest took place along the **(strand, shore)**.
11. The rope had unraveled so that only one **(strand, fray)** remained.
12. The miscount caused a **(hawk, fray)** as to who had won the election.

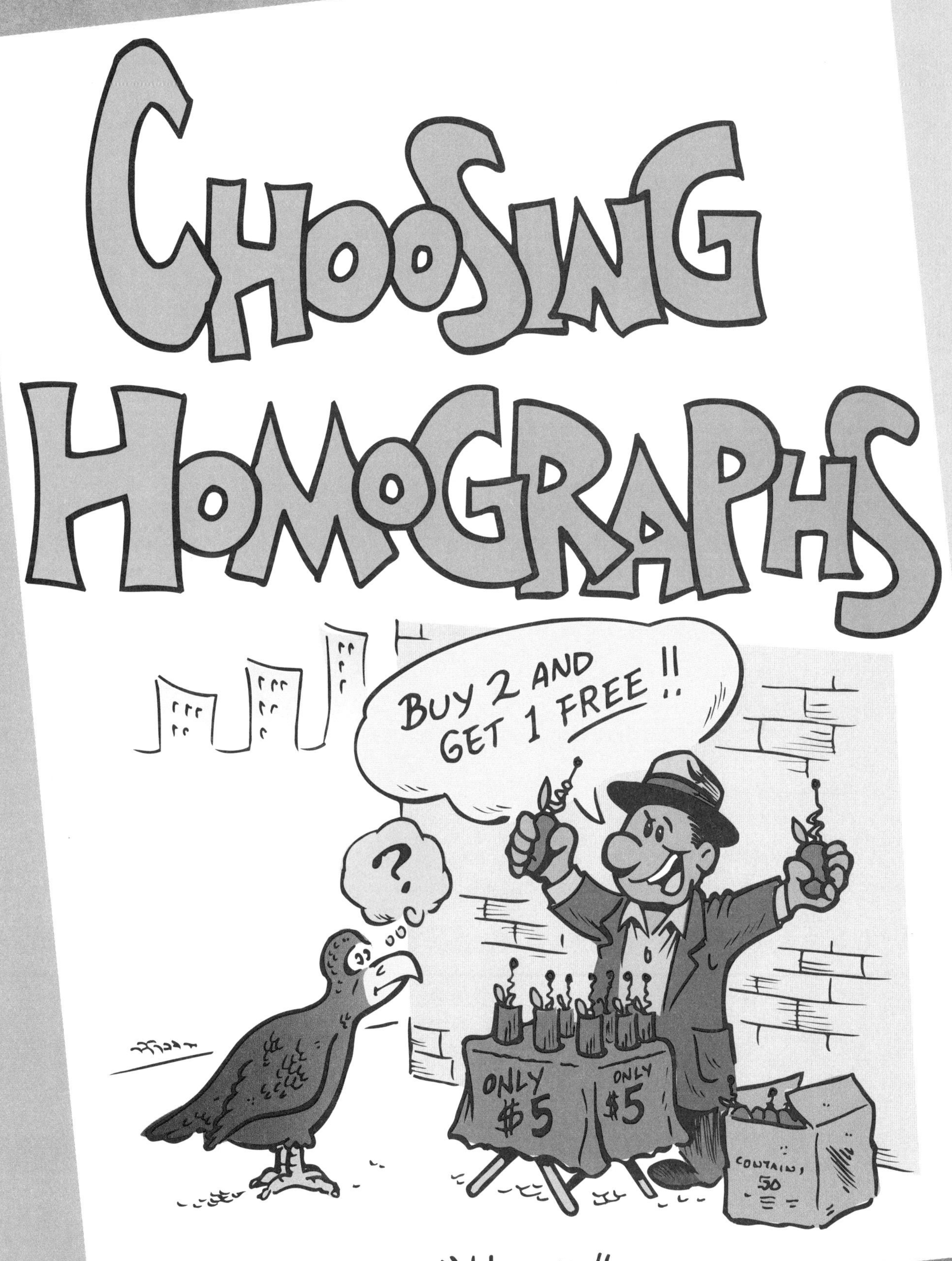
CHOOSING HOMOGRAPHS
BUY 2 AND GET 1 FREE !!
?
ONLY $5
ONLY $5
CONTAINS 50
"HAWK"

Choosing Homographs

Student Directions

Word Wiz

Homographs are two or more words that have the same spelling but different meanings.

In this center, the homographs are pairs of words used as both nouns and as verbs.

noun

A **hawk** glides on a breeze and soars for hours.

verb

His plan is to **hawk** Red Sox T-shirts and pennants and make enough money to pay his rent.

Follow These Steps

Partner Practice

1. Sort the cards into two piles—sentences and homographs.
2. Working together, read aloud the two sentences on a card. Find the homograph that correctly completes both sentences. Turn over the two cards to check your work.
3. Repeat Step 2 to match the other 11 sets of homographs and sentences.
4. Work together to complete your own activity sheet.
5. Check your work using the answer key.

Independent Practice

1. Sort the cards into two piles—sentences and homographs.
2. Read aloud the two sentences on a card. Find the homograph that correctly completes both sentences. Turn over the two cards to check your work.
3. Repeat Step 2 to match the other 11 sets of homographs and sentences.
4. Complete the activity sheet.
5. Check your work using the answer key.

Sonjay could recognize his horse by the ______ on its face.

The head of the school board aims to ______ a new path in preschool education.

The apple ______ produces a fragrance that attracts bees.

After months of lessons, Jake is beginning to ______ as a guitar player.

When a mother deer runs, the white underside of her tail acts like a signal for her ______ to follow her.

My sister's boyfriend tends to ______ over her and even runs her errands.

The guys got into a ______ over who hit the ball farther out of the park.

Are your jeans supposed to ______ at the knee, or are they torn from too much wear?

The red-tailed ______ flew in wide circles as it searched for prey.

I see the same people ______ souvenirs outside Wrigley Field every time I go to a game.

The ______ bobbed through the waves, spraying water on my face.

My aunt plans to ______ a new Internet business during the coming year.

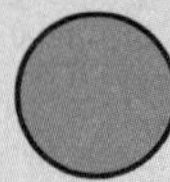

Choosing Homographs

EMC 3352 • © Evan-Moor Corp.

Choosing Homographs

EMC 3352 • © Evan-Moor Corp.

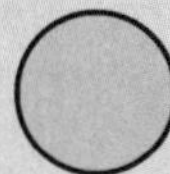

Choosing Homographs

EMC 3352 • © Evan-Moor Corp.

Choosing Homographs

EMC 3352 • © Evan-Moor Corp.

Choosing Homographs

EMC 3352 • © Evan-Moor Corp.

Choosing Homographs

EMC 3352 • © Evan-Moor Corp.

Bamboo _______ is becoming a popular choice for flooring.

Whenever Charlie's angry, you can hear him _______ up the stairs.

_______ is the color she chose for her brand-new car.

Pirates of old would _______ an enemy on a deserted island.

The conductor signaled the audience to sing the _______.

Remember your spending limit and _______ from buying another DVD.

Lily Beth likes to stroll the rugged coastal _______ when the surf is rough.

We can use those beams to _______ up the ceiling.

_______ trees are mashed into pulp before being pressed to make paper.

The doctor installed bright-colored shelves and a large saltwater aquarium to _______ up the waiting room.

Yikes! I pulled a _______ of yarn, and now one sweater sleeve is shorter than the other.

Furious tropical storms often _______ small boats on the beach.

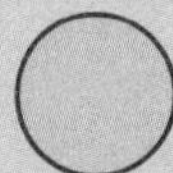

Choosing Homographs

EMC 3352 • © Evan-Moor Corp.

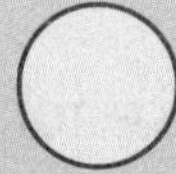

Choosing Homographs

EMC 3352 • © Evan-Moor Corp.

Choosing Homographs

EMC 3352 • © Evan-Moor Corp.

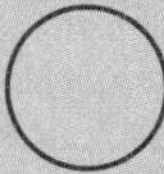

Choosing Homographs

EMC 3352 • © Evan-Moor Corp.

Choosing Homographs

EMC 3352 • © Evan-Moor Corp.

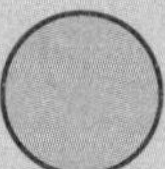

Choosing Homographs

EMC 3352 • © Evan-Moor Corp.

blaze

noun
a white mark on an animal's face

verb
to pioneer in a new direction or course

blossom

noun
the flower of a plant or tree that bears fruit

verb
to grow or improve

fawn

noun
a deer less than one year old

verb
to show exaggerated affection in order to be liked

fray

noun
a fight; a noisy quarrel

verb
to unravel

hawk

noun
a bird of prey with a hooked beak, sharp claws, and excellent eyesight

verb
to offer for sale on the street

launch

noun
a motorboat often used for sightseeing

verb
to begin or get going

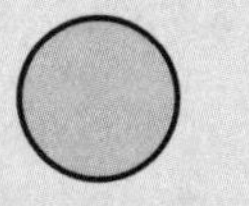

Choosing Homographs

EMC 3352 • © Evan-Moor Corp.

Choosing Homographs

EMC 3352 • © Evan-Moor Corp.

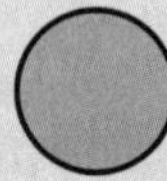

Choosing Homographs

EMC 3352 • © Evan-Moor Corp.

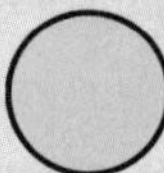

Choosing Homographs

EMC 3352 • © Evan-Moor Corp.

Choosing Homographs

EMC 3352 • © Evan-Moor Corp.

Choosing Homographs

EMC 3352 • © Evan-Moor Corp.

lumber

noun

wood or timber that has been sawed

verb

to move with a heavy step

maroon

noun

a dark reddish brown color

verb

to leave in a strange or isolated place

refrain

noun

a repeated part of a song or poem

verb

to hold yourself back from doing something

shore

noun

the land at the edge of a lake, river, ocean, or sea

verb

to support

spruce

noun

a type of evergreen tree often used to make paper

verb

to make tidy and appealing

strand

noun

an individual thread or wire that's twisted together to make yarn, rope, string, or cable

verb

to force onto a shore

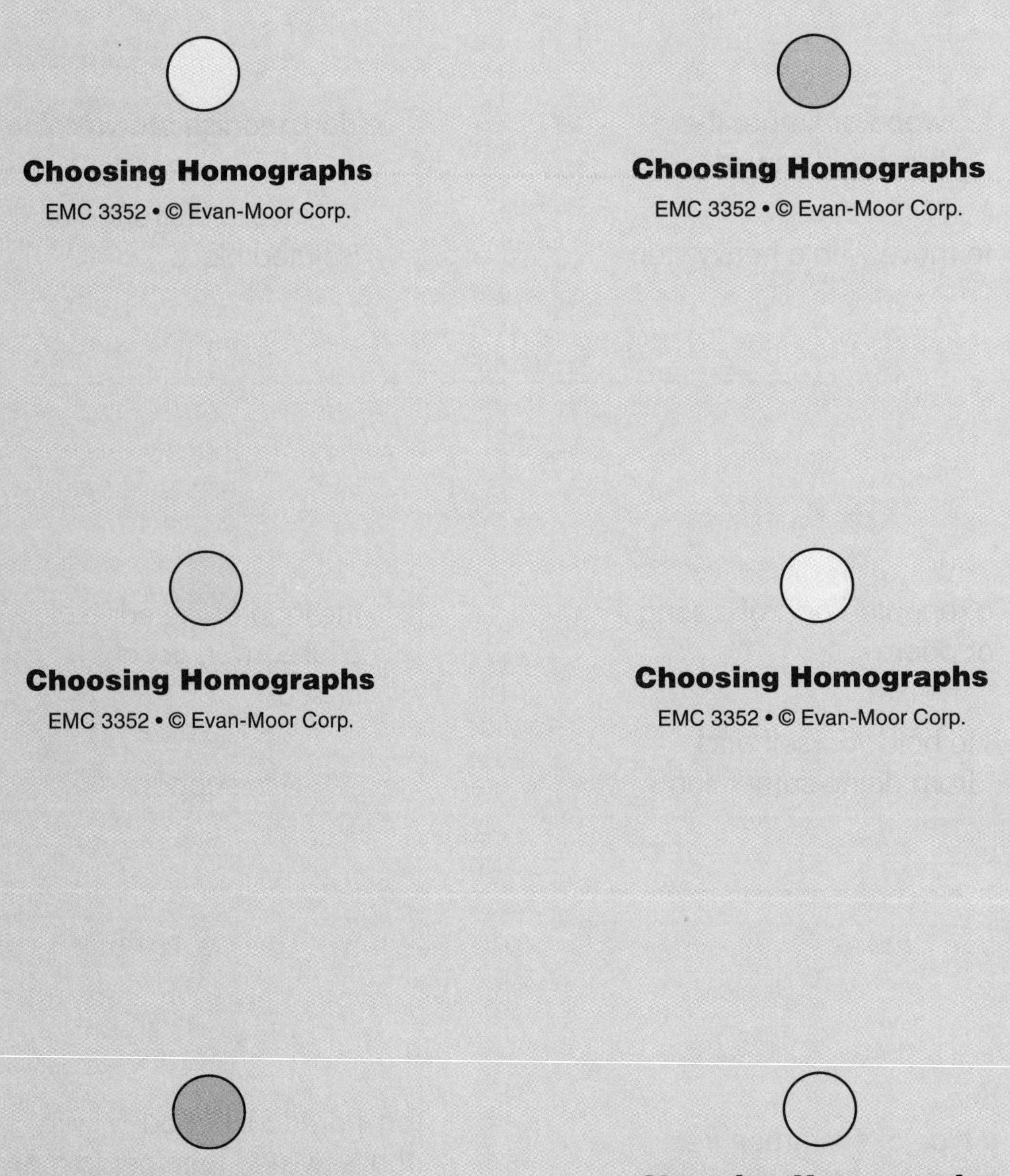

Choosing Homographs

EMC 3352 • © Evan-Moor Corp.

Choosing Homographs

EMC 3352 • © Evan-Moor Corp.

Choosing Homographs

EMC 3352 • © Evan-Moor Corp.

Choosing Homographs

EMC 3352 • © Evan-Moor Corp.

Choosing Homographs

EMC 3352 • © Evan-Moor Corp.

Choosing Homographs

EMC 3352 • © Evan-Moor Corp.

Answer Key

Lift the flap to check your answers.

Choosing Homographs

1. lumber
2. refrain
3. blossom
4. spruce
5. fawn
6. blaze
7. launch
8. hawk
9. maroon
10. shore
11. strand
12. fray